CAPT Science
(Third Generation)

Authors

Tanya Holst Arslanian
Wilton High School
Wilton, CT

Kathleen Mozak Pezza
Wesleyan University
Middletown, CT

Kenneth A. O'Konis
South Windsor High School
South Windsor, CT

Clyde Selner
South Windsor High School
South Windsor, CT

David P. White
South Windsor High School
South Windsor, CT

D1203832

Contributing Editors

Nur Abdulhayoglu
Housatonic Valley Regional High School
Falls Village, CT

Kathryn Eccleston
Putnam High School
Putnam, CT

Aart Hoogenboom
Wilton High School
Wilton, CT

Richard Therrien
Suffield High School
Suffield, CT

A "Get Smart Book®" from

WEBSTER HOUSE
PUBLISHING LLC
Ridgefield, CT

Library of Congress Control Number: 2004100949

ISBN: 1-932635-03-3

Printed in the United States of America

10 9 8 7 6 5 4 3

For additional information about Webster House Publishing LLC titles or "Get Smart Book®" titles, contact us on the Internet at http://www.websterhousepub.com, or write to Webster House Publishing LLC, Box 294, Georgetown, CT 06829.

Table of Contents

Introduction

What Is the CAPT?

The Connecticut Academic Performance Test (CAPT) is given in the spring to all Grade 10 students. It was first administered in 1994 to provide school systems and the public with feedback about a student's level of learning. The CAPT is part of a testing system that provides a logical progression from assessment of specific objectives at the lower grades to a focus on the integration and application of skills at the high school level. In addition to science, the CAPT includes sections on mathematics and reading and writing across the disciplines.

Test Format

The CAPT science section assesses science literacy by asking students to apply their knowledge of scientific content and principles. The science section consists of a combination of multiple-choice questions and open-ended questions (the latter require written responses). Students are asked to demonstrate their understanding of important concepts in five content strands and to apply those concepts in problem-solving situations.

In addition, experimentation skills are assessed by asking students to solve problems by using scientific reasoning. These questions largely relate to the ten curriculum embedded tasks completed in grades 9 and 10. Summaries of these activities are provided at appropriate points in this book.

The CAPT science section includes 65 total questions: 1 open-ended and 12 multiple-choice questions in each of the content strands. For each strand, 8 of the multiple-choice items assess content knowledge while 4 assess scientific inquiry, literacy, and numeracy.

Science inquiry is a major focus of the Third Generation CAPT Science Section. The science test assesses conceptual understanding and applications of scientific knowledge and experimentation in five content domains: (1) Energy Transformations; (2) Chemical Structures and Properties; (3) Global Interdependence; (4) Cell Chemistry and Biotechnology; and (5) Genetics, Evolution and Biodiversity. In each of these content domains, embedded tasks consisting of one inquiry lab and one science, technology and society activity are provided by the State Department of Education. Questions on the science section test students' understanding of the concepts and inquiry skills highlighted in these activities.

For ease of review, the content review in this book have been organized into core areas: Life Science, Physical Science, and Earth Science. A summary of each of the embedded tasks and its implications has been added.

The science test takes 100 minutes (broken into two 50-minute sessions).

Test Results

School districts receive sets of student reports that show how well individual students did on each section of the CAPT. Results are shared with students and their parents in October and November. Students receive a total score, and subscores are reported in Energy Transformation, Chemical Structure and Properties, Global Interdependence, Cell Chemistry and Biotechnology, Genetics, Evolution and Biodiversity, Content Knowledge, and Scientific Inquiry, Literacy and Numeracy. The test results are intended to help improve the performance of students, guide changes in curriculum and instructional practices, and stimulate higher expectations for achievement. The CAPT is not a high school graduation test. Students who meet the state goal standards on the CAPT receive a "Certification of Mastery" on their high school transcripts. Those who do not achieve the state standard in one or more areas can retake those parts of the test in Grades 11 and 12 and still gain "Certification of Mastery."

Scoring for Open-Ended Questions

The CAPT science section uses the following scoring rubric in assessing a student's response to an open-ended question:

Score 3

The response is an excellent answer to the question. It is correct, complete, and appropriate and contains elaboration, extension, or evidence of high-order thinking and relevant prior knowledge. There is no evidence of misconceptions. Minor errors will not necessarily lower the score.

Score 2

The response is a proficient answer to the question. It is generally correct, complete, and appropriate, although minor inaccuracies may appear. There may be limited evidence of elaboration, extension, high-order thinking, and relevant prior knowledge. There may be significant evidence of these traits but other flaws (e.g., inaccuracies, omissions, inappropriateness) may be more than minor.

Score 1

The response is a marginal answer to the question. While it may contain some elements of a proficient response, it is inaccurate, incomplete, or inappropriate. There is little if any evidence of elaboration, extension, high-order thinking, or relevant prior knowledge. There may be evidence of significant misconceptions.

Score 0

The response, although on topic, is an unsatisfactory answer to the question. It may fail to address the question, or it may address the question in a very limited way. There may be no evidence of elaboration, extension, high-order thinking, or relevant prior knowledge. There may be evidence of serious misconceptions.

Life Science

Chapter 1:
Ecosystems

A **species** consists of a group of related individuals that can intermate and produce fertile offspring. A group of individuals of the same species living in the same geographic area is referred to as a **population**. All of the organisms living in a given area with the potential to interact with one another constitute a **community**. An **ecosystem** can be defined as all of the organisms living in a given area (community), along with the abiotic (nonliving) factors with which they interact.

Nutrient and Energy Flow in Ecosystems

One-way Flow of Energy through an Ecosystem

Energy enters an ecosystem in the form of sunlight. The light energy reaching Earth is absorbed by plants and converted into chemical energy in the form of glucose through the process of **photosynthesis**. The equation below describes the reactants and products of photosynthesis:

$$6CO_2 + 12H_2O \xrightarrow[\text{chlorophyll}]{\text{light}} C_6H_{12}O_6 + 6O_2 + 6H_2O$$

carbon dioxide   water   glucose   oxygen   water

Chlorophyll pigments, found in the chloroplasts of leaf cells of green plants, absorb red and blue wavelengths of sunlight and reflect green wavelengths. This gives plant leaves their green color. The energy from the sunlight absorbed by chlorophyll molecules converts carbon dioxide, taken up through the plants' leaves, and water, taken up from the soil by plants' roots, into glucose molecules. As by-products of the reaction, oxygen and water are produced. The glucose molecules are used directly as an energy source or converted to more complex macromolecules, such as starch, for storage.

Organisms, such as plants, algae, and some bacteria, that are able to make their own food from chemicals and energy, are referred to as **autotrophs**. Animals and fungi are **heterotrophs**; they must consume other organisms to obtain energy. Autotrophs are often referred to as **producers**, because they produce their own food supply, while heterotrophs are often referred to as **consumers**, because they must consume other organisms to obtain food energy.

Energy stored in the cells of an organism is released for use by the organism through the process of **cellular respiration**. The energy-releasing reactions take place in the **mitochondria** and cytoplasm of an organism's cells and are summarized by the equation below (ATP = adenosine triphosphate):

$$\underset{\text{glucose}}{C_6H_{12}O_6} + \underset{\text{oxygen}}{6O_2} \longrightarrow \underset{\substack{\text{carbon} \\ \text{dioxide}}}{6CO_2} + \underset{\text{water}}{6H_2O} + ATP + heat$$

How Does Energy Move through an Ecosystem?

To answer this question, refer to Figure 1-1 below. Some of the energy made by plants during photosynthesis is transferred to heterotrophic organisms that consume the plants (**herbivores**). When an herbivore is eaten by another heterotroph (**carnivore**, or flesh-eating

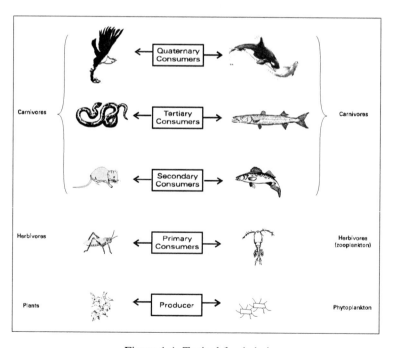

Figure 1-1. Typical food chains.

organism) a portion of the energy stored in the herbivore will be transferred to the carnivore. This chain of organisms, each consumed by another organism at successive levels, is called a **food chain**. At each level of the food chain, referred to as a **trophic level**, some of the energy is used up by the organism to maintain metabolic functions and some energy is lost to the surrounding environment as heat. At the end of the food chain are the **decomposers**—organisms such as fungi and bacteria that break down organic matter. As you can see, energy flows in one direction through food chains and must be resupplied to an ecosystem in the form of sunlight.

In addition to the transfer of energy within a food chain, toxins, such as heavy metals (mercury, lead, and others) released by human industry, are also transferred from one trophic level to the next, as the organism at the next higher trophic level consumes the one below it on the food chain. The toxins are usually concentrated in the fat or liver tissue of an organism; therefore, at each successive level of the food chain, the concentration of toxins in an organism's tissue is substantially increased. This increase in toxin concentration at successive levels of a food chain is referred to as **biological magnification**. Food chains do not exist as isolated entities in an ecosystem. Rather, several food chains interact to form what is known as a **food web**, as depicted in Figure 1-2. Some organisms eat both plants and animals and, therefore, can function as both **primary consumers** (feeding on autotrophs) and **secondary consumers** (feeding on heterotrophs). Decomposers act at each level of a food chain or food web, breaking down dead, decaying organisms.

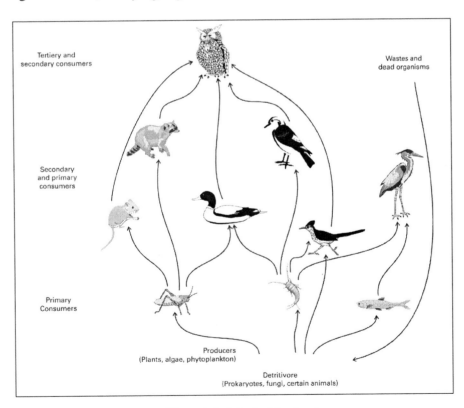

Figure 1-2. A typical food web.

Water and Chemical Nutrients Recycled in Ecosystems

While energy flows in one direction through an ecosystem, water and chemical nutrients such as carbon, oxygen, nitrogen, phosphorous, and calcium must be recycled in an ecosystem. These chemical cycles involve a circular movement of materials between **biotic** (living organisms) and **abiotic** (air, soil, water) components of an ecosystem. We will look at three examples of chemical cycling in an ecosystem: the nitrogen cycle, the carbon cycle, and the water cycle.

How Is Nitrogen Recycled in an Ecosystem?

Figure 1-3 depicts the process of nitrogen cycling in an ecosystem. The atmosphere, which is approximately 80% nitrogen, serves as the primary reservoir of nitrogen in an ecosystem. Unfortunately, atmospheric nitrogen is in the form of elemental nitrogen (N_2), while plants can only use nitrogen in the form of nitrate ions (NO_3^-) and ammonium ions (NH_4^+). Bacteria in the soil convert atmospheric nitrogen into a form that plants can take up from the soil and use to make amino acids and proteins. Animals that feed on the plants obtain nitrogen in the form of protein. When plants and animals die, decomposers break down the organic matter contained in the organisms, releasing nitrogen back into the soil that can be taken up by plants, or converted into elemental nitrogen by another group of bacteria (denitrifying bacteria) and released into the atmosphere.

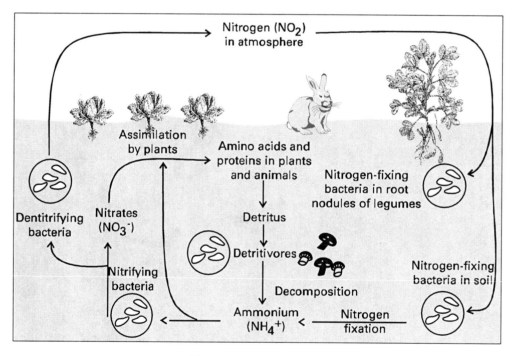

Figure 1-3. The nitrogen cycle.

How Is Carbon Recycled in an Ecosystem?

The carbon cycle is dependent on the processes of photosynthesis and cellular respiration. If you look at Figure 1-4, you can see that most of the carbon present in an ecosystem is cycled through the system in the form of carbon dioxide (CO_2). Because CO_2 is typically available in ample quantities in the atmosphere, an ecosystem is less likely to be depleted of carbon than of other nutrients, such as nitrogen or phosphorous, which may be lost to nutrient depleting processes such as deforestation. Carbon dioxide in the atmosphere is taken up by plants and converted into organic compounds that can be used by the plant to carry out metabolic functions, or taken up by animals that feed on the plants. Cellular respiration at each level of the food chain releases carbon back into the atmosphere in the form of CO_2. Decomposers also release CO_2 into the atmosphere during the breakdown of organic matter. In addition, CO_2 is released into the atmosphere as a result of burning wood and fossil fuels. On a global scale, the amount of CO_2 released during cellular respiration is roughly balanced by the uptake of CO_2 by plants during photosynthesis. However, the release of CO_2 into the atmosphere by the burning of wood and fossil fuels (coal and petroleum products) has greatly increased the concentration of CO_2 in the atmosphere above what can be removed by plants during photosynthesis, resulting in an excess level of CO_2 in the atmosphere.

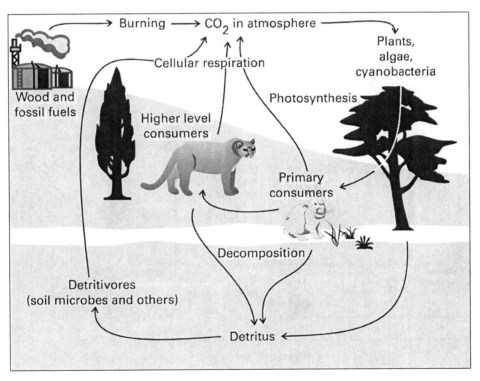

Figure 1-4. The carbon cycle.

How Does the Water Cycle Differ from the Other Chemical Cycles in an Ecosystem?

Although most organisms are composed largely of water, very little of the water cycling through an ecosystem is chemically changed by the organisms present, with the exception of the water molecules that are split during the process of photosynthesis. The water used in photosynthesis, however, represents a very small fraction of the water in an ecosystem. The water cycle is more of a physical process than a chemical one—primarily involving changes in state (gas, liquid, solid) than chemical changes. As such, the water cycle is quite different from the nutrient cycles (i.e., carbon, nitrogen, phosphorous) operating in an ecosystem. As you can see from Figure 1-5, on a global scale, evaporation exceeds precipitation over the oceans, resulting in a net movement of water from the oceans to the land. The water moves as water vapor, carried by prevailing winds, from the ocean to the land. Over land, there is an excess of precipitation relative to evaporation. This net precipitation over land results in the formation of surface and groundwater systems that flow back into the oceans. Approximately 90% of the evaporation over land is from plant transpiration (loss of water through stomata), with the remaining evaporation coming from surface water and other sources.

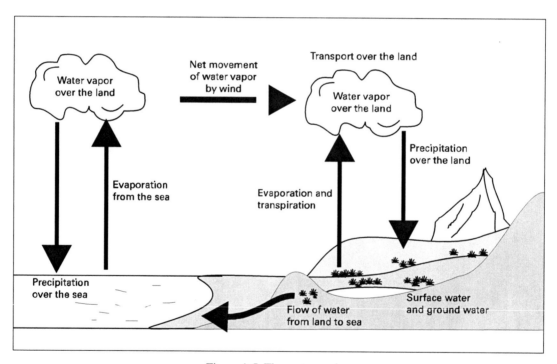

Figure 1-5. The water cycle.

CAPT Review Questions 1-4

1. Energy moves in one direction through an ecosystem and must be resupplied. The primary source of energy in an ecosystem is
   a. sunlight
   b. carbon
   c. glucose
   d. starch

2. The primary reservoir of nitrogen in an ecosystem is
   a. dead plant material
   b. dead animal carcasses
   c. the atmosphere
   d. bodies of water

3. Carbon is cycled through an ecosystem primarily in the form of
   a. glucose
   b. carbon dioxide
   c. decaying organisms
   d. complex organic compounds

4. A local subset of a species living together and interacting in a defined geographic area is referred to as a
   a. subspecies
   b. unit
   c. population
   d. community

Answers to CAPT Review Questions 1-4

1. **The correct answer is a.** The primary source of energy in an ecosystem is sunlight. Using the energy from the sun, autotrophs are able to make glucose from the carbon extracted from carbon dioxide. The glucose can then be used directly as fuel, or converted into starch for storage. Heterotrophs obtain energy by feeding on autotrophs or on other heterotrophs.

2. **The correct answer is c.** The atmosphere serves as the primary reservoir of nitrogen in an ecosystem.

3. **The correct answer is b.** Carbon is cycled through an ecosystem primarily in the form of carbon dioxide, through the processes of photosynthesis and respiration carried out by the organisms present.

4. **The correct answer is c.** A population is defined as a local subset of a species living together and interacting in a defined geographic area.

Population Ecology

A **population** is a local subset of a species living together and interacting in a defined geographic area. Populations of organisms and their growth are affected by the availability of resources, competition among organisms for limited resources, and climate changes. Different organisms are adapted to the different environmental conditions present in various regions.

Population density is the number of individuals of a particular species present in a defined area or volume. For example, the number of people per square kilometer (km^2) in a rural town defines the population density of that town.

What Factors Contribute to the Density of a Population?

One important factor that contributes to the density of a population is the availability of resources (e.g., food, water, shelter). The larger the population, the more resources it takes to sustain it. Population-limiting factors such as food supply, which affect a greater percentage of individuals as the number of individuals in the population increases, are referred to as **density-dependent factors**. Such factors affect population growth by increasing the death rate, decreasing the birth rate, or both. Other density-dependent factors affecting population growth include limited availability of water, limited space for shelter and reproduction, and a buildup of toxins in the ecosystem. **Density-independent factors** that limit population growth are not affected by population density. These include such things as climate and weather (e.g., freezes, droughts, floods), fires, and volcanoes. Density-independent factors affect the same percentage of the population regardless of population density.

When resources are limited, individuals must compete for the available resources in an area. Such competition may occur between individuals of the same species (**intraspecific competition**) or between individuals of different species (**interspecific competition**). As resources become limited, intraspecific competition for food, water, or shelter may result in a decrease in the density of a population, as certain individuals are less able to compete for food, water, or shelter. When two or more populations of different species occupy an area and compete for the same resources, growth of both populations may decline. Sometimes, one of the species will be eliminated from the community.

What Are Some of the Ways in Which Different Species in a Community Interact?

Interactions in which one species (**predator**) consumes another species (**prey**) are referred to as **predation**. An example of predation would be the consumption of rabbits by foxes living in the same area. A special type of predation, known as **parasitism**, occurs when one organism (**parasite**) lives on or within another organism (**host**) from which it obtains food—for example, a tapeworm living in the intestine of a mammalian host. Occasionally, species evolve what is known as a **mutualistic** relationship in which both species benefit from the interaction. One example of a mutualistic relationship is that of a **lichen**. A lichen is actually composed of a particular fungal species and a particular algal species living together in a mutualistic relationship in which the alga photosynthesizes and produces food for both components and the fungus absorbs water and minerals from the soil, which are used by both components.

Adaptation of Different Organisms to the Environmental Conditions in Different Geographic Regions

In addition to studying local (community) ecosystems, we can look at the ecosystem on a global level. The global ecosystem— the **biosphere**—includes all the living (biotic) and nonliving (abiotic) entities on Earth. The biosphere extends several kilometers into the atmosphere and several kilometers beneath the Earth's surface. The biosphere is subdivided into various terrestrial and aquatic regions, each with characteristic plants and animals living there.

What Determines the Distribution of Plants and Animals in a Region?

The primary abiotic factors that influence what organisms live in a particular region are solar energy, water, temperature, and wind. Other abiotic (not biotic) factors that play a role in the distribution of species include hurricanes and tornadoes, fires, droughts, and so on.

Solar energy is the light energy from the sun that drives photosynthesis, providing energy to most terrestrial and aquatic ecosystems. Only those ecosystems found in areas where sunlight does not reach (hydrothermal vents, caves) are not dependent on solar energy; they derive energy from inorganic chemicals extracted by bacteria. The amount of sunlight reaching an area influences the amount and composition of vegetation capable of existing there. The amount of sunlight reaching a desert region is quite different from that reaching the ground in a densely forested area.

Water is essential to all living organisms. The amount of water an area receives determines the diversity of organisms living there. Fresh and saltwater ecosystems contain very different organisms, as do deserts and tropical rainforests.

Temperature affects the metabolism of organisms, and therefore, the average high and low temperatures in a given ecosystem determine which organisms live there. Different species have adaptations that allow them to adapt to very cold or very warm temperatures, which affects their distributions.

Wind has many affects on an ecosystem and the organisms that live there. Some sedentary organisms rely on winds to blow in food or nutrients. The evaporative cooling effect of wind increases the amount of water lost by an organism.

The various terrestrial ecosystems on Earth are referred to as **biomes**. Each biome is a large geographical region defined by the dominant vegetation found there and the organisms adapted to that particular set of conditions (solar energy, water, temperature, and wind patterns). The particular species found in each biome are those that are adapted to the conditions present in that region. In some cases, a species will evolve in the region, becoming better and better adapted to the local conditions over time. Other times, a species will move into an area from another area and survive in the new area because of preexisting adaptations to the new area.

What Are Some of the Major Impacts of Humans on Ecosystems?

The human species has a significant impact on the health and functioning of the biosphere. The activities of humans often disrupt normal patterns of chemical/nutrient cycling in an ecosystem. The introduction of chemicals (e.g., pesticides, cleaners, industrial toxins) that are not a natural part of the ecosystem cause many species to develop abnormally or have lower rates of reproduction. Human activities also result in a disruption of nutrient cycles by adding excessive amounts of certain nutrients to some areas and depleting nutrients from other areas. For example, the clear-cutting of forested areas (the removal of all trees from a stand of timber) removes large quantities of carbon and inorganic nutrients from a region. Overfertilization of agricultural and urban lands allows excess nutrients, particularly nitrogen and phosphorous, to run off into lakes and streams. The excess nutrients allow for an overgrowth of aquatic plants. Competition for resources causes many of the plants to die and sink to the bottom of the lake or stream. As decomposers break down the organic material in the dead plants, they consume large quantities of oxygen, depleting the amount of oxygen available for other aquatic organisms and causing massive die-offs. The excessive plant growth caused by excess nutrient runoff is referred to as **eutrophication**.

The burning of wood and combustion of fossil fuels release sulfur and nitrogen oxides into the atmosphere, where they react with water to form sulfuric and nitric acid. The acids eventually fall back to Earth as acid precipitation. The acidity of the precipitation (rain or snow) lowers the pH of aquatic ecosystems, as well as alters the soil chemistry of terrestrial ecosystems. Many species of fish and other aquatic organisms drastically decreased in population and health in aquatic ecosystems that have been acidified by acid precipitation. In terrestrial ecosystems, the change in soil pH due to acid precipitation causes many nutrients to be leached from the soil or converted into chemical forms that are no longer available to the plants growing in the area. The resulting nutrient deficiencies affect the growth and health of the plants in the area.

The combustion of fossil fuels may also lead to global changes in climate through the release of excessive amounts of carbon dioxide into the atmosphere. While carbon dioxide is transparent to visible light, it intercepts and absorbs much of the infrared light reradiated from Earth's surface, trapping solar heat in the lower atmosphere nearer Earth's surface. While this **"greenhouse effect"** is critical in maintaining a hospitable environment for the organisms on earth, it is now thought that excessive amounts of carbon dioxide in the atmosphere may lead to an overall increase in global temperatures over time, resulting in an alteration of climate patterns.

Human activities also are responsible, at least in part, for depleting the ozone levels in the atmosphere. Ozone molecules form a protective layer in the lower stratosphere that absorbs ultraviolet (UV) radiation from the sun, preventing much of the damaging radiation from reaching the biosphere. The protective ozone layer has been shown to be thinning over time since the mid-1970s. Researchers believe the thinning is due primarily to the release of chlorofluorocarbons, chemicals used in refrigeration and as aerosol propellants. The breakdown products of chlorofluorocarbons, particularly chlorine, react with ozone, reducing the ozone to oxygen, which does not have the protective effects against UV radiation. Scientists predict that severe thinning of the protective ozone layer may lead to increases in the rates of skin cancer and cataracts among humans, as well as unpredictable effects on other organisms.

CAPT Review Questions 5-7

5. A lichen is an example of which of the following interspecific interactions?
   a. Predation
   b. Parasitism
   c. Mutualism
   d. Competition

6. The global ecosystem is referred to as the
   a. biosphere
   b. biome
   c. atmosphere
   d. stratosphere

7. The burning of wood and combustion of fossil fuels release sulfur and nitrogen oxides into the atmosphere. These chemicals may eventually return to Earth as
   a. acid precipitation
   b. ozone
   c. smog
   d. global warming

Answers to CAPT Review Questions 5-7

5. **The correct answer is c.** A lichen represents a mutualistic relationship between an alga and a fungus, in which both organisms benefit from the relationship. In predation, one organism feeds on another organism; parasitism is a special form of predation in which the parasite lives on or in a host organism; competition involves two or more organisms competing for limited resources.

6. **The correct answer is a.** The global ecosystem is referred to as the biosphere. A biome is a large geographical region defined by the dominant vegetation found there and the organisms adapted to that particular set of conditions (e.g., solar energy, water, temperature, wind patterns).

7. **The correct answer is a.** The sulfur and nitrogen oxides released into the atmosphere through the burning of wood and fossil fuels reacts with water in the atmosphere to form sulfuric and nitric acid. These acids are returned to Earth in the form of acid precipitation.

Curriculum Embedded Performance Task

Strand V: Genetics, Evolution, and Biodiversity Laboratory

Yeast Population Dynamics

In this laboratory, you designed an experiment to test the effects of environmental factors on the growth of a population. The state task calls for the use of yeast, a one-celled fungus, that is able to reproduce quickly in a small space. Population growth is measure by measuring the production of carbon dioxide bubbles produced as the yeast perform cellular respiration to obtain energy for growth and reproduction. The more yeast, the more respiration being performed, and the more carbon dioxide that should be present in the tube.

Factors that can be tested are the effects of food availability (molasses) in the test tube, the pH level of the test tube, and the temperature of the test tube. As you review this laboratory, consider the following questions:

1. What is the independent variable? The dependent variable?
2. What type of graph would be appropriate for graphing the data obtained in this lab?
3. What can the shape of your graph tell you about the underlying variables being measured?
4. What features of this experiment were you able to control?
5. How were you able to control these features?
6. What features of this experiment were not able to be controlled? Why?
7. How confident are you in the results of this experiment?
8. How valid is this experiment? Remember to consider how well the designed experiment measures the stated problem, the ability to control the experiment, the amount of data collected, and the reliability of the collected data.

Curriculum Embedded Performance Task

Strand V: Genetics, Evolution, and Biodiversity Science, Technology, and Society

Human Population Dynamics

In this embedded task you selected two countries to study; a developed nation, and a developing nation. You were asked to consider the size of the populations of each country, their growth rates, and the shapes of their growth curves. As you compared these features, you also considered the possible underlying reasons for the differences between the two countries' populations.

Chapter 2:
Genetics and Evolution

Genetic Basis of Inheritance

Genetics is the study of how genes bring about characteristics or traits in living organisms. The cells of living organisms contain **DNA (deoxyribonucleic acid)**, which determines the characteristics of the organism. The DNA is contained in one or more **chromosomes**. Bacterial cells usually contain a single circular chromosome, while most other organisms have several chromosomes that are found within a cellular structure called a **nucleus**. DNA is composed of sugar molecules (deoxyribose), phosphate groups, and four nitrogenous bases: adenine, cytosine, guanine, and thymine. Alternating sugar and phosphate groups form a backbone, while the nitrogenous bases form hydrogen bonds with each other, holding the two backbones together. Adenine and thymine bond with each other, while cytosine and guanine bond with each other, in what is known as **complementary base pairing**. The whole structure is twisted upon itself to form a **double helix** (Figure 2-1).

Along the DNA molecule are stretches of the five purine (i.e., adenine, guanine) or pyrimidine (i.e., cytosine, thymine, uracil) bases that code for specific characteristics. These regions are referred to as **genes**. Each **gene** is a hereditary unit of information containing a specific nucleotide sequence of **DNA** and, thus, is responsible for determining a particular characteristic in an individual. Each gene can exist in several forms, called **alleles**. For example, a gene for flower color may be in the form (allele) that codes for red flower color, or in the form (allele) that codes for white flower color.

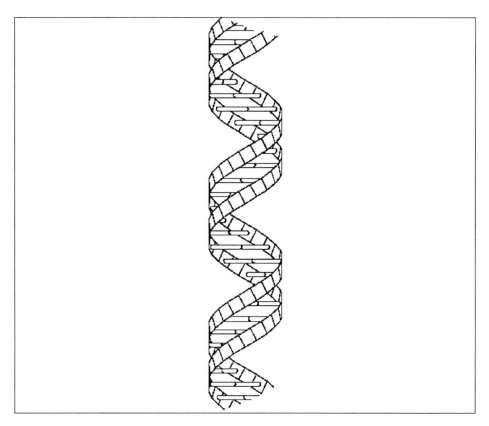

Figure 2-1. The structure of the DNA molecule.

How Are the Coded Messages Contained in the Genes on a DNA Molecule Expressed as a Characteristic of an Individual?

Lets take the example of flower color above. The region of DNA coding for flower color will have a certain sequence of nitrogenous bases that specifies whether the individual will have red or white flowers. However, in order for the flower color to be expressed in an individual, it must be converted into proteins that are, in turn, expressed as a pigment. This is a two-step process: (1) **transcription**—the transfer of genetic information from a DNA molecule to an RNA molecule, and (2) **translation**—the transfer of information contained in the RNA molecule into a protein. In transcription, the genetic message on the DNA molecule is copied onto a molecule of **RNA (ribonucleic acid)** in the nucleus. This **messenger RNA (mRNA)** molecule leaves the nucleus and attaches to a **ribosome** in the cell's cytoplasm. Ribosomes are composed of **ribosomal RNA (rRNA)** and proteins, and are the sites where translation occurs. While the mRNA is attached to the ribosome, **transfer RNA (tRNA)** molecules, each of which has an **amino acid** attached to it, will briefly bind the to mRNA at sites where the tRNA sequence is complementary to the mRNA sequence. Figure 2-2 below illustrates the processes of transcription and translation.

The site along the chromosome where a gene is located is referred to as a **locus**. Some alleles mask the expression of alternate alleles at the same locus when both alleles are present

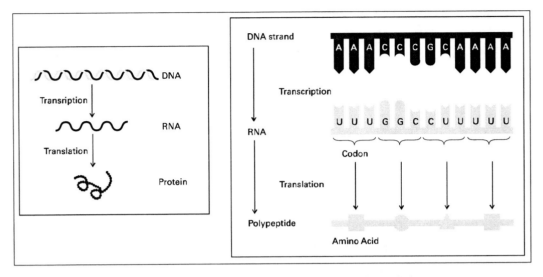

Figure 2-2. The processes of transcription and translation.

together. These are referred to as **dominant** alleles and are designated by a capital letter (e.g., A). Alleles that are masked by the presence of dominant alleles are referred to as **recessive** alleles and are designated by a lowercase letter (e.g., a). All of the alleles present in the genome of an individual, regardless of their form (dominant or recessive), constitute the **genotype** of that individual. The physical appearance or biological characteristics of an individual is referred to as the **phenotype** and is determined by which alleles are expressed at each locus. The phenotype also may be influenced by the environmental conditions to which the individual is exposed.

How Is an Individual's Phenotype Determined?

An individual inherits one allele from each of its parents. Humans have 46 chromosomes in each of their cells, with 23 chromosomes inherited from their father through the sperm and 23 chromosomes inherited from their mother through the egg at fertilization. If an individual inherits a dominant allele from each parent, they are said to be **homozygous dominant** for that trait (AA). If an individual inherits two recessive alleles, they are referred to as being **homozygous recessive** (aa). If an individual inherits one dominant allele and one recessive allele, they are referred to as being **heterozygous** for that trait (Aa).

Let's look at an example. If red flower color ® is **completely dominant** to white flower color ®, an individual with a phenotype showing red flowers could have the genotype RR or Rr, while a white-flowered individual could only have the genotype rr. In some traits, the dominant allele does not completely mask the recessive allele. When present together in the heterozygous condition, the phenotype is usually intermediate between the two homozygous phenotypes. This is referred to as **incomplete dominance** (as opposed to **complete dominance**, as described in the example above). For example, if the allele for red flower color did not completely mask the allele for white flower color, heterozygous individuals (Rr) would have pink flowers.

In certain other traits, both alleles may be expressed to some degree in heterozygous individuals. This is referred to as **codominance** and is most often seen at the biochemical level. An example of codominance is the existence of the A, B, AB, and O blood groups in humans. These blood groups are based on the presence of two specific molecules on the surfaces of red blood cells. A single gene with two alleles is responsible for determining which blood type an individual expresses. Individuals who have the "A" phenotype are homozygous for the A allele and produce one type of molecule on the surfaces of their red blood cells. Individuals with the "B" phenotype are homozygous for the B allele. These individuals also produce one type of molecule on the surfaces of their red blood cells. However, it is different from that produced by "A" individuals. Individuals with the "AB" phenotype are heterozygous and produce both types of molecules on the surfaces of their red blood cells. Individuals with the type "O" phenotype are homozygous for the O allele. These individuals have neither A, B, nor O molecules on the surface of their red blood cells.

Genotypes and Phenotypes of Individuals Predict the Genotypes and Phenotypes among Offspring

The Augustinian monk, **Gregor Mendel**, developed the science of genetics based on experiments he conducted in the 1860s and 1870s; however, his work was not widely accepted by the scientific community until early in the twentieth century. Mendel developed a method for predicting the outcome of inheritance patterns by conducting genetic experiments on pea plants. Pea plants pollinate themselves, and after several generations of self-pollination, individual plants that are homozygous for particular traits will be produced. These individual plants are considered true-breeding or pure lines.

In his work, Mendel took several pure lines of peas and cross-pollinated them with other pure lines and followed the inheritance patterns of different traits through several generations of offspring. Mendel called the pure lines he started with the **parental generation**. One thing he noticed was that when he crossed pure-line tall plants with pure-line short plants, all of the offspring plants were tall. Mendel called this first generation of offspring the **first filial** or F_1 **generation**. Next, Mendel crossed several of the F_1 plants together to produce the **second filial**, or F_2 **generation**. In the F_2 generation, he observed that three-fourths of the plants were tall and one-fourth of the plants were short, as illustrated below.

Parental generation:	Tall × Short
F_1 generation:	All Tall
Inter-mating F_1s	Tall × Tall
F_2 generation:	$1/4$ Tall; $1/4$ Short

How Are Genotypes and Phenotypes Predicted in Offspring?

To predict the possibility of a particular trait being inherited by offspring, several steps are followed. First, a symbol is designated for each allele of the gene. The dominant allele is represented by a capital letter and the recessive allele by the corresponding lowercase letter. In keeping with our previous flower color example, we could designate the allele for red flower color "R" and the allele for white flower color "r". For a homozygous dominant individual, the genotype would be "RR"; for a heterozygous individual, the genotype would be "Rr"; and for a homozygous recessive individual, the genotype would be "rr".

The next step in performing a genetic cross is determining the genotypes of the parents and the genotypes of the gametes. If two heterozygous parents are crossed (Rr × Rr), each parent could produce gametes containing *either* a dominant allele ® or a recessive allele ®, and each type of gamete would be produced in roughly equal frequency. To predict the genotypes and phenotypes of the offspring between these two parents, a **Punnett square** could be used. The possible gametes produced by the female parent are indicated at the top of the square and the possible gametes produced by the male parent are indicated to the left of the square. Thus, for the cross between two heterozygous parents, Rr × Rr, the Punnett square would be as in Figure 2-3A:

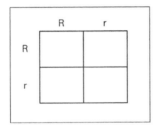

Figure 2-3A. Punnett square for Rr × Rr.

To determine the possible genotypes of the offspring, all possible combinations of gametes must be considered. This is done by combining the gamete at the top of each cell of the square with the gamete to the left of the cell, as illustrated below in Figure 2-3B:

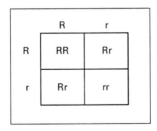

Figure 2-3B. Possible genotypes.

From the Punnett square, we can see that $\frac{1}{4}$ of the offspring will be homozygous dominant (RR), $\frac{1}{2}$ of the offspring will be heterozygous (Rr), and $\frac{1}{4}$ of the offspring will be homozygous recessive (rr). Therefore, the offspring from the cross between the two heterozygotes would produce offspring with a **genotypic ratio** of 1:2:1 (1 RR:2 Rr :1 rr). Because red flower color is dominant over white flower color, the heterozygous individuals, as well as the homozygous dominant individuals will have red flowers, and only the homozygous recessive individuals will have white flowers. Therefore, the **phenotypic ratio** among the offspring is 3:1 (3 with red flowers:1 with white flowers).

Mendel conducted several more experiments following the inheritance of various traits—either one trait at a time or pairs of traits simultaneously. Over many years of conducting such experiments, Mendel developed several principles of inheritance that are known today as Mendel's principles of genetics.

In populations of organisms, genetic variation is enhanced when the genes carried in the gamete from one parent combine during fertilization with genes carried in the gamete from another parent. This results in the formation of offspring with a new combination of genes than was present in either of the parents. In other words, genes are transmitted through **gametes** from parents to offspring, with new genetic combinations coming together when the gametes unite to form a **zygote**. Thus, the genetic characteristics of an organism are established at fertilization with the union of the male and female gametes.

What Is DNA Fingerprinting?

The characterization of an individual's DNA (**DNA fingerprinting**) is currently being used to identify the source of human DNA in paternity suits and criminal cases, as well as in the diagnosis and treatment of genetic diseases. The military is in the process of establishing a DNA "databank" to ensure the identification of any personnel that may otherwise become "unknown soldiers" during combat situations. Several states have set up similar databanks documenting convicted felons in their prison systems. Sources of DNA samples used in fingerprinting include blood, skin, semen, hair, and, in some instances, preserved bone tissue.

How Are DNA Fingerprints Produced?

DNA fingerprints can be produced by digesting DNA samples with a **restriction enzyme** and separating the resulting DNA fragments by **gel electrophoresis**. With some imagination, the bands produced in a DNA fingerprint resemble bar codes found on commercial products sold in stores. Just as the bar codes are used to identify the manufacturer and the individual product, DNA fingerprints can be used to identify family relationships and distinguish among individuals within a family. If the positions of all the variable fragments of a DNA sample match those of a suspect (or inmate, or soldier), computer analysis is used to determine the probability of such a match occurring by chance. **Restriction enzymes** are naturally found in bacteria where they destroy foreign DNA molecules that invade the bacterial cell (e.g., DNA from other bacterial cells or from bacterial viruses). They work by cleaving the foreign DNA molecules at specific sites (this process is referred to as **restriction**). Each restriction enzyme recognizes a different short sequence on the DNA molecule, usually four to six base-pairs long, and cleaves the molecule each time it encounters that specific sequence (referred to as a

restriction site). Bacteria protect their own DNA from restriction by adding methyl groups to the recognition sequences for the specific restriction enzyme(s) they contain. Different strains of bacteria have different restriction enzymes specific to that strain.

No two individuals, other than identical twins, have the same DNA. Therefore, when DNA samples from different individuals are digested with the same restriction enzyme and subjected to gel electrophoresis, different fragment patterns (DNA fingerprints) will be produced. If DNA samples form a mother, father, and their child are digested with the same restriction enzyme, the patterns of each individual would be different, but the child's DNA pattern would have some fragments in common with each parent (Figure 2-3C).

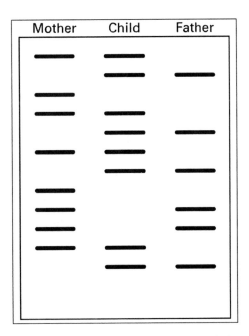

Figure 2-3C. DNA banding patterns produced by restriction enzyme digestion of genomic DNA from a mother, a father, and their child.

What Are the Potential Problems with the Use of DNA Fingerprinting Analysis?

Potential problems with DNA fingerprinting analysis include the possibility of contamination or degradation of the DNA sample(s). Most research laboratories use pure DNA samples for analysis, however, the DNA samples used in forensic studies are often hours, days, or even years old. The samples may be contaminated by bacteria, fungi, or organic material, or they may be exposed to unfavorable conditions of light or temperature, causing the DNA sample to degrade. Although contamination and degradation may make it difficult to obtain a large enough DNA sample for positive identification, it is not possible to identify the wrong individual from a contaminated or degraded sample. When small or degraded samples of DNA are collected, the samples can be amplified (several thousand identical copies made) through a process known as the **polymerase chain reaction (PCR)**. This allows an adequate quantity of DNA for further analysis, such as DNA fingerprinting.

Can Genes Be Manipulated?

In the last 50 years or so scientists have developed the ability to manipulate DNA in such a way as to alter the behavior and physiology of a variety of organisms. In the same time period, medical researchers have developed the means for removing faulty cells from sick individuals, adding a normal copy of the faulty gene to those cells in the laboratory, and then placing those cells back into the patient as a form of gene therapy.

What Are Transgenic Organisms?

Transgenic organisms are those organisms that have a foreign gene inserted into their DNA. First, researchers must determine the genetic sequence of a desirable gene in an organism that they want to transfer to a different, often unrelated, organism. For example, suppose scientists wanted to create frogs that glow in the dark, they might start by sequencing the gene responsible for bioluminescence in jellyfish. To get the bioluminescence gene into the frogs, they would need to manufacture a segment of DNA in the laboratory with the same sequence as the bioluminescence gene and insert the sequence into a **vector**. A vector is used to insert the gene of interest into a bacterial colony, which will produce numerous copies of the gene as the bacterial cells reproduce. The most common vectors used are **plasmids**, small circular DNA molecules typically found in bacterial cells, and **phages**, viruses that attack bacteria. The gene of interest would then be isolated from the bacterial colony and purified and inserted into frog cells using a gene gun. The gene gun uses microscopic pellets of gold or tungsten coated with DNA containing the gene of interest, which are blasted into frog cells in culture.

Curriculum Embedded Performance Task

Strand IV: Cell Chemistry and Biotechnology Science, Technology, and Society

Bioengineered Foods

Bioengineered foods are any foods that come from plants or animals that have been altered genetically in any way. Bioengineering can be as simple as choosing which plants or animals are allowed to mate and reproduce, and as complex as the addition of specific genes from other organisms. In this task, you examined the potential positives and negatives to the genetic engineering of food, from the production of plants that are more resistant to pests or lack of water, to the potential increase of environmental steroids in our diets and atmosphere. In this activity, and in any well-reasoned science argument, you must acquire and use the available evidence to make a good decision about whether or not to label foods that have been in some way engineered. While the underlying positions on either side are simple (for those who wish to label, the right of knowledge of the consumer is most important, while those who do not wish to label worry that too much consumer knowledge may lead to panic), the ability to provide ample and good evidence is not.

CAPT Review Questions 1-4

1. The structure of a DNA molecule can best be described as
   a. a linear chain of alternating sugars, phosphate groups, and nitrogenous bases
   b. a single helix consisting of a backbone of alternating sugar and phosphate molecules with nitrogenous bases facing the inside
   c. a double helix consisting of a backbone of alternating sugars and nitrogenous bases held together by phosphate groups
   d. a double helix consisting of a backbone of alternating sugars and phosphate groups held together by nitrogenous base pairs

2. Which of the following correctly depicts the conversion of the genetic code into protein?
   a. RNA (translation) → DNA (transcription) → protein
   b. RNA (transcription) → DNA (translation) → protein
   c. DNA (translation) → RNA (transcription) → protein
   d. DNA (transcription) → RNA (translation) → protein

3. If brown fur color shows incomplete dominance over while fur color in squirrels, then heterozygous individuals would most likely have
   a. brown fur, because the gene for brown fur would mask the gene for white fur
   b. bodies that have brown fur on one side and white fur on the other side
   c. fur with brown and white spots
   d. tan fur

4. DNA fingerprinting is currently being used to
   a. identify the source of human DNA in paternity suits
   b. identify the source of DNA in criminal cases
   c. diagnose and treat certain genetic disorders
   d. do all of the above

Answers to CAPT Review Questions 1-4

1. **The correct answer is d.** The DNA molecule is represented by a double helix composed of a backbone consisting of alternating sugar and phosphate molecules with nitrogenous base pairs holding the backbone together.

2. **The correct answer is d.** The conversion of the genetic code into protein starts with the DNA molecule in the nucleus, which is transcribed onto a mRNA molecule. The mRNA moves out of the nucleus and attaches to a ribosome, where translation of the message on the mRNA into protein occurs.

3. **The correct answer is d.** With incomplete dominance, the heterozygote will have an intermediate phenotype between the brown homozygotes.

4. **The correct answer is d.** DNA fingerprinting is currently used to identify sources of DNA in paternity suits and criminal cases, as well as in the identification and treatment of certain genetic disorders.

The Evolution of Species

The **gene pool** of a population reflects the total complement of genes in a population at a given time. The gene pools of populations are not static; rather, their composition changes over time as their members live and die. As an organism in a population dies, its unique genetic composition is lost. Thus, a population changes in genetic composition over time—and this is the biological concept behind **evolution**. The fundamental force that gives rise to the diversity of animal species is evolution by **natural selection**. In the mid-1800s, **Charles Darwin** and **Alfred Wallace** independently (and virtually simultaneously) proposed the theory of evolution by natural selection to explain how organisms change through natural processes acting over long periods of time. The theory of natural selection is based upon the following points:

1. Individuals in a population vary extensively in their characteristics; no two individuals are exactly alike.
2. Much of the variation among individuals is heritable (can be passed on from parent to offspring).
3. All organisms have great reproductive potential and their populations would increase exponentially if all individuals who were born survived and reproduced; however, populations tend to remain relatively stable in size over time.
4. Natural resources are limited.
5. The production of more individuals than the environment can support leads to a struggle for existence among individuals in a population with only a fraction of offspring surviving each generation.
6. Those offspring that inherit characteristics most suitable to their environment are more likely to survive and leave more offspring than individuals who are less adapted to their environment.

Traits that allow an individual to survive and reproduce will be passed on to the individual's offspring. Therefore, individuals who are better adapted to their environment will be more likely to reproduce and preferentially pass on those genes to the next generation.

The ability to survive and reproduce is referred to as **reproductive fitness**. Thus, if certain inherited traits provide an advantage of one individual over another in a given environment, then that trait would provide a reproductive advantage to the individual. This concept is sometimes referred to as "survival of the fittest."

To summarize, natural selection can be defined as a "differential success in reproduction." After several generations of natural selection, the traits will change within the population (the population has evolved). Over a longer time period, new species may originate through natural selection in different environments.

This final point has important consequences for plant and animal diversity. Individual species vary naturally in numerous characteristics. Imagine a population (an interbreeding group) of an insect-eating bird species. Some birds have longer, slender bills (like a woodpecker), others may have shorter, stout bills (like a finch). Those birds with slender bills may be favored through natural selection in an area where insects live in small holes in the wood. The stout-billed variety may be favored where large, armored beetles are abundant (as the stout beak can exert more force). Even though these varieties began in the same population, the varieties may segregate in space, or in behavior, such that they mate preferentially with similar varieties, thereby forming two distinct populations. If a particular variety occupies the "unsuitable" habitat, it may either die or not reproduce well. The offspring of the two varieties may become increasingly different, perhaps with longer and shorter bills, respectively. The variants also become more different in the frequencies of the genes that underlie these and other traits. This change in gene frequencies, and ultimate changes in physiology or behavior, is evolution. Thus, evolution can result from natural selection taking place over a long period of time.

Besides Natural Selection, What Other Mechanisms Influence Evolution in Populations?

Another way that species may evolve occurs through the process of chance. Within species, chance effects occur by processes such as **genetic drift**. Genetic drift will occur when small parts of a population are isolated from the larger population of the same species (such as when some individuals become lost and eventually settle in a new area). The genetic variation within this "new" population is typically much less than in the original population from which it was derived. Genetic drift may also occur when a small group of individuals leaves the population and establishes a new population in a geographically isolated region. This small group of individuals typically represents only a small portion of the original gene pool, and the genetic variability in this "new" population is usually quite low (**founder effect**). Over time, these individuals may become reproductively isolated from the original population and develop into a separate species. Similarly, genetic variation is greatly reduced when a population goes through a **genetic bottleneck** (such as when all but a few individuals of a population are eliminated by a natural disaster, loss of habitat).

Migration of individuals into (or out of) a population, from (or to) other populations that have different allelic and genotypic frequencies, can also alter the allelic and genotypic frequencies within the original population. Migration of individuals into or out of a population results in gene flow between two or more populations. When migrating individuals mate with native individuals, they contribute their genes to the gene pool of the local population. The migrating individuals often bring in new traits that were not previously present in the local population.

Another important force in evolution is **mutation**, in which a gene (the chemical code for a trait) changes in structure or function, resulting in an organism with an altered behavior or physical structure. Mutations may be harmful and selected against, or they may be beneficial and confer a selective advantage for an individual. The individuals with the advantageous mutation will show greater reproductive fitness than those without the mutation.

What Is the Primary Evidence Supporting Evolution?

Several pieces of evidence strongly support the theory of evolution. In science, a **theory** refers to a widely accepted explanation of a variety of related phenomena that have withstood repeated testing and experimentation.

One piece of evidence comes from **paleontology**—the study of fossils. The **fossil record** shows evidence of a descent of modern organisms from common ancestors.

More evidence for evolution comes from the study of **comparative anatomy**. For example, the forelimbs of such diverse animals as humans, porpoises, cats, birds, and bats are strikingly similar, even though the forelimbs are used for very different purposes (i.e., lifting, swimming, flying). The various modifications are thought to be adaptations to the specific needs of modern organisms that all arose from a common ancestor. Also, many organisms have structures they do not use. Often, these structures are degenerate and undersized compared with similar structures in other organisms. The useless structures are called **vestigial organs**. In humans, they include the appendix, the fused tail vertebrae, and the wisdom teeth. It is possible that environmental changes made the organs unnecessary, and the organs gradually became nonfunctional and reduced in size.

Embryology offers additional evidence for evolution. The embryos of fish, reptiles, chickens, rabbits, and humans share many similarities. For example, all have gill slits, a two-chambered heart, and a tail with muscles. This uniformity provides evidence of evolutionary relationships in that diverse organisms have all inherited the developmental mechanisms of a common ancestor. In the later stages of embryo development, the organisms appear less and less similar.

Studies in modern **biochemistry** indicate there are biochemical similarities among all living organisms. For example the mechanisms for transferring energy and building proteins from amino acids are nearly identical in all organisms. DNA and RNA serve as the basis for inheritance in all living organisms, and the structure of the genetic code is virtually identical in all living systems. The uniformity in biochemical organization points to evolutionary relationships among organisms.

CAPT Review Questions 5-6

5. A change in the genetic composition of a population over time is referred to as
   a. natural selection
   b. evolution
   c. gene pool shuffling
   d. reproductive fitness

6. Migration of individuals into or out of a population can lead to
   a. changes in the allele frequencies in the original population
   b. changes in genotypic frequencies in the original population
   c. evolution of a new species
   d. all of the above

Answers to Review Questions 5-6

5. **The correct answer is b.** Evolution reflects a change in the genetic composition of a population over time. Natural selection is one mechanism by which evolution may occur.

6. **The correct answer is d.** Migration of individuals into or out of a population may lead to changes in the allelic and genotypic frequencies in the original population and, ultimately, to the evolution of a new species.

Chapter 3:
Cells

Cell Structure and Function

All living (or once living) organisms are composed of cells from microscopic, single-celled organisms (e.g., bacteria) to large organisms composed of billions of cells (e.g., people). Many types of cells exist, but there are some basic characteristics that all cells have in common:

1. Cells are self-contained—each is surrounded by a **cell membrane**, which sets the boundary of the cell and controls the passage of materials into and out of the cell. The presence of the membrane allows the cell to be distinct from its surroundings both chemically and structurally.
2. Inside the membrane is the **cytoplasm**, a term used to describe the jelly-like substance that surrounds the contents of the cell.
3. Cells of living organisms also contain **DNA** (deoxyribonucleic acid)—the material responsible for genetic inheritance.

An organism is placed into one of two broad categories based on the organization of its cells; specifically, whether or not the DNA and other materials are organized and compartmentalized within the cytoplasm. **Eukaryotic cells** have their DNA organized and packaged in multiple linear chromosomes, and the chromosomes are collectively surrounded by a membrane separating them from the rest of the cytoplasm. This membrane-bound compartment is called the **nucleus**. Eukaryotic cells also have other compartments that are surrounded by membranes; this allows them to carry out specific functions in an "isolated environment" within the cell. These structures are referred to as **organelles** and include **mitochondria, plastids, Golgi apparatus, endoplasmic reticulum**, and **peroxisomes**.

Prokaryotic cells are far more simple in structure and organization than are eukaryotic cells. They lack a distinct nucleus. With a few exceptions, the DNA of prokaryotes is organized into one circular chromosome. Organisms that are composed of prokaryotic cells are referred to as **prokaryotes**, while those composed of eukaryotic cells are called **eukaryotes**.

Plant cells contain several features not found in animal cells. In addition to organelles common to all eukaryotes, plant cells contain organelles called **plastids** that carry out specialized functions, such as pigment production, storage of starch, and **photosynthesis**. Plant cells are surrounded by rigid **cell walls**; animal cells do not have cell walls. (Fungi, algae, and most bacteria also have cell walls.) Most plant cells contain a large **central vacuole**, filled with **cell sap**, where various metabolic products are stored. The vacuole also plays a role in maintaining water balance in plant cells. If present in animal cells, vacuoles are small and numerous.

The typical structure of a cell is shown in Figure 3-1 below.

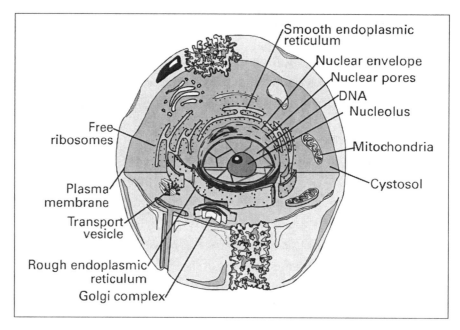

Figure 3-1. Typical structure of a cell.

What Are the Primary Functions of the Major Cellular Organelles?

The primary functions of the major cellular organelles are defined below:

Nucleus: The nucleus houses the chromosomes of a cell. These chromosomes contain the genetic information that determines the characteristics of an individual.

Ribosome: The ribsome is the site of protein synthesis.

Mitochondria: The mitochondria are the sites of cellular respiration, which produces energy (ATP) necessary for carrying out metabolic functions.

Chloroplast: Choloroplasts are the sites of photosynthesis, which makes food in the form of sugar for the organism; they are found only in cells of plants, algae, and some bacteria. Cholorplasts are not found in the cells of animals or fungi.

Chromoplast: Chromoplasts contain red, orange, and yellow pigments responsible for the color of some flowers and fruits; they are found only on plant cells.

What Are the Structures and Functions of the Major Cell Types Found in Humans?

Let's look at the structure and function of four of the major cell types found in humans.

Skin cells: Human skin cells typically form sheets of loosely packed cells called **epithelium**. The skin, also known as **dermal tissue**, forms the outer covering of the human body. The skin serves as a first line of defense against invading organisms. The outer layer of intact skin is composed of a layer of dead cells that most viruses and bacteria are unable to penetrate. The skin also serves as a sensory organ, containing receptors for temperature, touch, and pressure.

Nerve cells: Human nerve cells are referred to as **neurons** and are specialized for carrying signals throughout the body. Neurons interact with each other, forming large networks capable of carrying signals from one region of the body to another, allowing us to perceive and respond to our environment, to learn and remember. Neurons typically have a large cell body from which two types of fibers extend—**dendrites**, which are short and highly branched, and **axons**, which are larger and nonbranching. Dendrites pick up signals and convey them to the neuron body. Axons, of which there may be only one per cell, conduct signals toward another neuron or toward an **effector** (a cell, tissue, or organ capable of carrying out a response to a nervous system signal).

Muscle cells: Muscle tissue is composed of bundles of long cells called muscle fibers. There are three main types of muscle tissue in humans: (1) **skeletal muscle**, which is attached to the bones by tendons and allows for movement; (2) **smooth muscle**, which lines the walls of human organs; and (3) **cardiac muscle**, which forms the contractile tissue of the heart.

Blood cells: Blood consists of cells suspended in plasma. There are three basic types of cells found in the blood—red blood cells, white blood cells, and platelets. **Platelets** are pieces of cell cytoplasm that have pinched off of large cells in the bone marrow and are important for blood clotting. **Red blood cells**, called **erythrocytes**, are shaped like concave disks, which suits their main function of transporting oxygen and carbon dioxide throughout the body. **White blood cells**, called **leukocytes**, play a role in the body's immune system by fighting off infectious agents and helping to control the growth of cancerous cells.

Control of the Movement of Substances into and out of the Cell by the Plasma Membrane

The ability of a cell to take in and expel substances is essential to its survival. Regulation of movement of materials across cellular membranes occurs because the membranes are

differentially permeable—they only allow certain **types** of substances to pass through, and they control the **rate** at which they pass through. Some substances are **actively** moved through the cell membrane by a process known as **active transport**. Such movement requires an input of energy. Other substances can **passively** move across the membrane if the membrane is permeable to those substances. Selected substances passively move across the membrane by **diffusion**—the dispersion of a substance in a system by the movement of its molecules. **Kinetic energy** causes molecules to disperse from a region of high concentration to a region of low concentration. Dispersion of molecules will continue until the distribution is homogeneous throughout the solution, as depicted below in Figure 3-2.

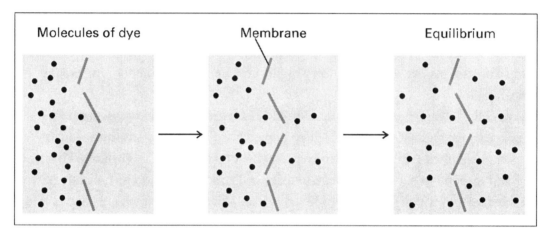

Figure 3-2. Diffusion of substances across a differentially permeable membrane.

The movement of substances into and out of a cell's environment and many of the physiological processes that occur in organisms involve diffusion phenomena. Only a few substances (i.e., gases, water) readily move unaided across cell membranes by diffusion. Most molecules move across cell membranes by **facilitated diffusion** and require the aid of a specific membrane protein (or proteins).

The diffusion of **water** across a differentially permeable membrane from a region of high (water) concentration to a region of low (water) concentration is referred to as **osmosis**. If a cell is placed in pure water, the cell will take up water because the concentration of water outside the cell (pure water) is greater than the concentration of water inside the cell (cell sap, which contains dissolved substances). If the water concentration inside the cell is greater than the water concentration outside the cell—for example, if a cell is placed in concentrated salt water—the cell will lose water to the environment. Plant and animal cells respond differently to changes in the water concentration in their environment. When animal cells are placed in pure water, they will continue to take up water and swell until they burst. When placed in concentrated salt water, animal cells will dehydrate and shrivel. Because of the presence of the cell wall, when plant cells are placed in pure water, they will take up water and the membrane-bound cell will begin to swell, until it reaches a point where the cell wall exerts pressure back on the cell membrane, forcing excess water out of the cell. This pressure exerted by the cell wall— known as **turgor pressure**—allows nonwoody plants to remain erect.

CAPT Review Questions 1-2

1. Which of the following organelles is correctly paired with its function?
   a. nucleus—protein synthesis
   b. ribosome—contains the genetic material
   c. mitochondria—cellular respiration (ATP production)
   d. chloroplast—gets rid of cellular waste

2. Cellular membranes help control what moves into and out of cells because the membranes are
   a. not permeable to any substances
   b. permeable to all substances
   c. differentially permeable to various substances
   d. allow only water to pass through them

Answers to CAPT Review Questions 1-2

1. **The correct answer is c.** Cellular respiration occurs in the mitochondria of plant and animal cells. The nucleus contains the genetic information for the cell in the form of DNA; ribosomes are the sites of protein synthesis; and chloroplasts are the sites of photosynthesis in plant cells.

2. **The correct answer is c.** Cellular membranes help control what moves into and out of cells because the membranes are differentially permeable, allowing some substances to pass through but not others.

Cell Division

Cell division is the process in which a single cell divides, giving rise to two daughter cells. These daughter cells expand and may eventually divide, each giving rise to two new cells. It is through these ongoing processes of cell division and expansion that growth, repair, and reproduction occur. When cell division occurs, it is necessary that the components of the parent cell be distributed equally between the two daughter cells so they will function normally. Each daughter cell must end up with a **nucleus** containing a complete set of **chromosomes** identical to the parent cell. The chromosomes are the "blueprint" for the building and maintenance of a cell; an incomplete or incorrect set results in a faulty cell. After successful cell division the two daughter cells are genetically identical to the parent cell from which they originated. Two things occur that ensure the inheritance of one complete set of chromosomes by each daughter cell:

1. The chromosomes must be duplicated or copied. This process is called **DNA replication** and results in two copies of each chromosome within the cell.

2. One copy of each chromosome must be distributed to each new cell. This is accomplished through the process known as **mitosis.**

The **cell cycle** describes the relative time frame for the occurrence of DNA replication and mitosis in a single cell (Figure 3-3). It consists of four phases:

1. Mitosis, the division of the nucleus
2. G1, the gap in time between mitosis and replication, during which cell growth occurs
3. S, the phase in which synthesis of DNA occurs (DNA replication)
4. G2, the gap in time between replication and the next mitotic phase

G1, S, and G2 collectively are known as **interphase**, the period of time between mitotic divisions. The longest period of the cell cycle is **interphase**. This is the period between cell divisions. The nucleus is visible with a nuclear envelope. Individual **chromosomes** cannot be distinguished. DNA **replication** occurs during interphase.

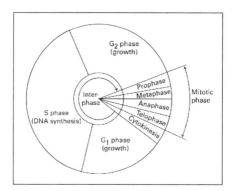

Figure 3-3. Diagrammatic representation of the relative time period for each phase of the cell cycle, based on a 24-hour cycle (G = gap, S = synthesis).

Mitosis and Cytokinesis

There are four stages of mitosis: prophase, metaphase, anaphase, and telophase. These are depicted below, along with a brief description of what occurs in each phase.

1. **Prophase:** Prophase is the first stage of mitosis. In prophase, the chromatin begins to condense, and individual chromosomes become visible. Because DNA replication has already taken place (during interphase), each chromosome consists of two **sister chromatids** joined at the **centromere**. The nuclear envelope begins to break down. During this stage the **spindle apparatus** forms (Figure 3-4).

2. **Metaphase:** The chromosomes move along the **spindle fibers** to the center of the cell. This central region is referred to as the **metaphase plate**. You should be able to distinguish the two sister chromatids (copies) of each chromosome.

3. **Anaphase**: During anaphase, the sister chromatids separate at their centromeres, and each is pulled to an opposite end of the cell by contraction of the spindle fibers. At the end of anaphase, each pole of the cell contains a complete set of chromosomes.

4. **Telophase:** The final stage of mitosis begins when the chromosomes reach the opposite ends of the cell and stop moving. During this stage, the spindle apparatus disappears, and the chromosomes become diffuse.

Cell division is not complete unless **cytokinesis** accompanies mitosis. Between the two new nuclei a **cell plate** (in plant cells) or a **cleavage furrow** (in animal cells) forms. Nuclear envelopes form around the two new nuclei at each end of the cell. Two daughter cells are now distinguishable in place of the original parent cell. The two daughter cells are genetically identical to each other, and each daughter cell is genetically identical to the original parent cell.

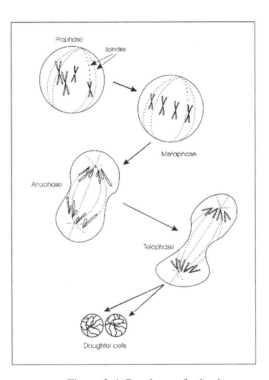

Figure 3-4. Prophase of mitosis.

Meiosis

The life cycle of most eukaryotic organisms includes **sexual reproduction**, where two cells (**gametes**) fuse during **fertilization** to form a single-celled **zygote**, which then develops into a new organism. When two gametes fuse during fertilization to form a zygote, the resulting individual contains twice as many chromosomes as either parent cell (gamete)—generally consisting of two sets of chromosomes, one set from each parent cell. In order for the number of chromosomes of a species to remain **constant** from generation to generation, some process must occur to reduce the number of chromosomes in the gametes before they fuse to form a zygote. This reduction in chromosome number is accomplished by the process of **meiosis**, a special type of **cell division**. Meiosis leads to the formation of gametes, each of which has half the number of chromosomes as its parent cell. Therefore, when two gametes unite to form a zygote, the original number of chromosomes for that organism is reestablished. To achieve this, the process of meiosis divides the chromosomes **twice** (instead of once, as occurs in mitosis—somatic cell division—which you studied previously).

As stated above, meiosis results in specialized cells that have a reduced number of chromosomes. Most organisms are **diploid**; that is, they have **two sets** of chromosomes (which are reproduced in **each** cell of the organism's body via mitosis). Meiosis, on the other hand, **only** occurs in specialized **"sex cells"**—cells that eventually give rise to gametes. During meiosis, the ploidy level of the cell is reduced by one-half; the resulting cells each have **one set** of chromosomes and are referred to as **haploid**. **Ploidy** is a genetic condition where there are more than two of a particular chromosome. When haploid cells fuse they form a diploid zygote, thereby restoring the original (diploid) condition to the new organism.

Meiosis consists of **two successive nuclear divisions**. The first nuclear division, which is usually accompanied by cytokinesis, is referred to as **meiosis I**. The second nuclear division, also typically accompanied by cytokinesis, is referred to as **meiosis II**. Both meiosis I and meiosis II have the four "phases" you observed in mitosis: **prophase**, **metaphase**, **anaphase**, and **telophase**. To distinguish between the phases of the two successive divisions, the numerals I and II are used (e.g., prophase I or prophase II).

Meiosis I is the nuclear division in which the number of chromosomes is reduced, as the two chromosomes of a homologous pair are separated from each other and packaged into separate (haploid) daughter cells. **Meiosis II** is a nuclear division similar to mitosis, where **sister chromatids** separate from each other. Upon completion of meiosis, **four haploid cells** are produced as a result of the two successive nuclear divisions.

Another important feature of meiosis is the ability of chromosomes to exchange genetic information during a certain phase of meiosis (prophase I), which leads to **genetic variation**. When meiosis occurs, the resulting nuclei are **genetically distinct** from one another. Again, this is different from what we observed during the process of mitosis in which the resulting daughter cells were **identical** to each other, as well as to the parent cell.

The phases of meiosis are depicted below, along with a brief description of what occurs in each phase.

Meiosis I

Prophase I: During early prophase I, the chromosomes begin to condense and become visible. The nuclear envelope breaks down and begins to disappear. As prophase I continues, the chromosomes become shorter and thicker, **chromatids** become visible, and the **pairing of similar chromosomes** from each set takes place. The chromosomes that pair (**homologues**) carry genes for the same traits; this causes their three-dimensional structures to be very similar and allows them to "find each other" during pairing. The pairing of homologous chromosomes during prophase I is referred to as **synapsis**. The difference between homologous chromosomes is that the **alleles** (alternative forms of the same gene) may differ. It is during this stage that **chromatids** from homologous chromosomes may twist around each other. It is in these regions that **genetic exchange (crossing over)** occurs.

Metaphase I: Paired chromosomes line up in the **center** of the cell at the metaphase plate (equatorial plane). Formation of the **spindle apparatus** is complete.

Anaphase I: Paired chromosomes begin to **separate** and **one chromosome from each homologous pair** is pulled to **opposite ends** of the cell. This ensures that **each daughter cell** receives **one complete set** of chromosomes.

Telophase I: The nuclear envelopes reform, and cytokinesis usually takes place at the completion of telophase.

A short interphase period may follow meiosis I, **but no additional DNA replication will occur.**

Meiosis II

Meiosis II follows the short interphase that takes place after meiosis I. It is essentially like a mitotic division; however, the ploidy of the "parent cell" cell is now haploid.

1. **Prophase II:** The spindle apparatus reforms, chromosomes condense, and the nuclear envelope disappears in each cell. No synapsis occurs.
2. **Metaphase II:** The chromosomes line up randomly in the center of each cell.
3. **Anaphase II:** Centromeres split apart and sister chromatids are pulled to opposite ends of the cells.
4. **Telophase II and Cytokinesis:** Sister chromatids are now at opposite ends of the cell and are considered to be individual chromosomes. A cell plate (plant cells) or cleavage furrow (animal cells) forms between daughter cells.

Plants and animals have slightly different life cycles. In animals, meiosis gives rise directly to gametes. In plants, meiosis gives rise to spores, which germinate and develop into a multicellular stage, called the **gametophyte**. The gametophyte produces gametes, which fuse to form a zygote, or **sporophyte** phase. Typical animal and plant life cycles are depicted in Figure 3-5.

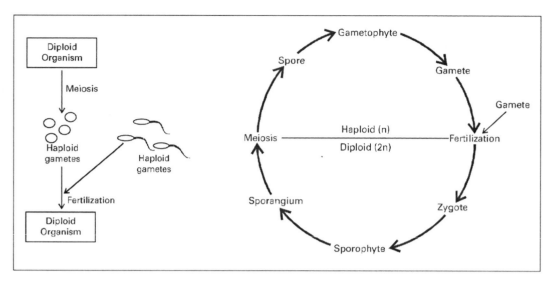

Figure 3-5. Typical animal life cycle *(left)* and plant life cycle *(right)*.

CAPT Review Questions 3-4

3. Which of the following statements regarding mitosis is incorrect?
   a. It results in the production of genetically identical daughter cells.
   b. It is necessary for growth of an organism.
   c. It plays a role in the repair of tissue damage.
   d. It leads to the production of sperm and eggs.

4. An organism with 24 chromosomes in each of its cells would produce gametes containing
   a. 24 chromosomes
   b. 12 chromosomes
   c. 6 chromosomes
   d. 3 chromosomes

Answers to CAPT Review Questions 3-4

3. **The correct answer is d.** Meiosis, not mitosis, leads to the production of sperm and eggs.

4. **The correct answer is b.** During the production of gametes through the process of meiosis, the number of chromosomes is reduced by one-half. Thus, a gamete would have 12 chromosomes.

Cell Chemistry

Enzymes

What is a protein? A protein is a biological polymer made up of monomers called amino acids. There are 20 naturally occurring amino acids used by living organisms. When the amino acids are bonded together in long chains, the order of amino acids determines the shape that the protein will take. Many proteins used by living things consist of hundreds to thousands of amino acids folded into shapes that determine what function each protein will have.

What is an enzyme?

Enzymes are protein catalysts made by cells. Every chemical reaction done by cells occurs with the help of an enzyme. The shape of each enzyme allows it to assist one specific reaction and speed that reaction without the need for heating the chemicals involved. These chemicals, when being catalyzed by an enzyme, are known as substrates. Because of its shape, every enzyme is specific for certain substrates. Because the enzyme itself is not changed by the reaction, but rather just helps to break and assemble bonds, each enzyme can be reused many times until it is broken down by the cell.

How do enzymes work?

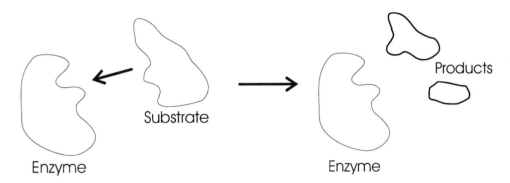

Figure 3-6. The enzyme combines with a substrate to form a substrate complex. They bond together like a "key in a lock." As the link weakness, a new product is formed and is released from the active site of the enzyme. The process then begins over again.

What factors affect the rate of enzyme catalyzed reactions?

Because an enzyme's function is determined largely by the shape into which it has folded, any factor that alters the shape of the protein with alter its ability to act. While heating generally helps to speed chemical reactions (including those that are enzyme-catalyzed), extreme heating, especially to the boiling point of water, will cause an enzyme to denature (or unfold). What remains is a chain of bonded amino acids, incapable of functioning as a catalyst.

The addition of chemicals that may disrupt weak forces that hold together the folded protein will also cause an enzyme to denature. For instance, the addition of alcohols such as ethanol can get in the way of hydrogen bonding, causing proteins to unfold and stop working.

Curriculum Embedded Performance Task

Strand IV: Cell Chemistry and Biotechnology Laboratory

Enzymes

In this laboratory, you designed an experiment to test the effectiveness of two enzymes, and a mixture of these enzymes on the production of apple juice from apple sauce. As you consider this experiment, you should remember that enzymes are able to work only on particular chemicals, known as substrates, that have the correct shape to help to catalyze a reaction. Remember to think about which reactions pectinase and cellulose are able to catalyze as you analyze the reasons that either or both helps to release more juice from the apple sauce. Remember also to consider the following questions as you think about any experiment:

1. What is the independent variable? The dependent variable?
2. What type of graph would be appropriate for graphing the data obtained in this lab?
3. What can the shape of your graph tell you about the underlying variables being measured?
4. What features of this experiment were you able to control?
5. How were you able to control these features?
6. What features of this experiment were not able to be controlled? Why?
7. How confident are you in the results of this experiment?
8. How valid is this experiment? Remember to consider how well the designed experiment measures the stated problem, the ability to control the experiment, the amount of data collected, and the reliability of the collected data.

Chapter 4: Microorganisms

Bacteria?

Bacteria are single-celled organisms. All bacteria are prokaryotic cells, meaning that they are small, primitive cells lacking a true nucleus. About the size of one mitochondrion from a eukaryotic cell, bacteria have a single, circular chromosome made of DNA as their genetic material. Bacteria are able to reproduce themselves in a process known as binary fission, in which the bacteria first copies its chromosome, and then the cell divides in a process in which the cell membrane pinches off separating the cytoplasm and membrane into two separate, smaller cells.

Where do bacteria live?

In short, bacteria are everywhere, and serve many purposes, and have many niches in ecosystems. While we tend to be most familiar with parasitic bacteria such as Streptococcus pneumoniae, a bacterium that lives and grows in the alveoli of the lungs causing illness and some types of pneumonia, many bacteria are necessary to our survival and the function of ecosystems.

Mutualistic strains of E. coli live in our digestive system, allowing us to properly digest our foods and absorb the nutrients. In return, these bacteria are provided with a place to live and ample supplies of the nutrients they need. Other bacteria live in the soil and the root nodules of legume plants, helping to fix nitrogen from an unusable form (nitrogen gas) to a form that plants are able to use to build amino acids and nucleic acids (ammonium ion).

Viruses?

Viruses are not cells. Most viruses consist of a piece of genetic material (either DNA or RNA), surrounded by a coat of protein. The protein coat of a virus allows some protection for its genetic material, but, more importantly, allows the virus to trick living cells. This trickery is necessary because, unlike bacteria, viruses are not able to reproduce themselves. Because of their inability to reproduce themselves, viruses do not meet the traditional definition of "living".

How do viruses enter cells?

Viruses trick a cell's own receptors. Every cell has receptors on its membrane designed to recognize food and other molecules that the cell needs. These receptors trigger various reactions in the membrane that allow these molecules to enter the cell. Through the shape and structure of its protein coat, a virus is able to resemble the intended molecule, tricking the cell into allowing it in. Because different types of cells have different functions and different needs, they also have different receptors designed to recognize different molecules. As a result, many viruses are specific for the types of cells that they can infect. Human Immunodeficiency Virus (HIV, the virus that causes AIDS), is only able to infect human immune cells by the name of T cells.

The structures of individual viruses also result in varying methods of transmission. Some viruses, like HIV, are not able to become airborne. HIV is only able to travel from one host to another through the exchange of bodily fluids. Other viruses are able to become airborne, and are strong enough to survive on surfaces for significant periods of time. Influenza, the scientific name for the virus we know as the flu, is able to spread through air.

How do viruses reproduce?

In order to reproduce itself, a virus must trick a cell into allowing its genetic material to enter. Once this has occurred, the virus's DNA takes over the machinery of cell, turning it into a virus-producing machine. The cell manufactures viral DNA (sometimes mistaking some host DNA for viral DNA, allowing the virus to mutate), and protein coats.

What are antibiotics, and when do they work?

Antibiotics are molecules that are toxic to bacteria, preventing them from growing and reproducing. These molecules are cytotoxic, meaning that they are toxic to cells. Since viruses are not cells, antibiotics do not work to prevent or curtail infection by a virus. The first antibiotics discovered, by accident, came from living organisms called molds. Alexander Fleming noted that mold growing on his bacterial plates seemed to prevent the growth of bacteria in the areas that they were growing. The compound isolated from this mold was penicillin.

What is antibiotic resistance?

When antibiotics are used to treat a bacterial infection, the first bacteria to succumb to the toxins are those that are most sensitive to the toxins we have added. Over time, more bacteria die, and eventually, the bacteria that were least sensitive to that antibiotic may also be killed. When antibiotics are misused, though, we unintentionally help bacteria to evolve resistance. For instance, in the first few days of antibiotic use (penicillin is usually prescribed in a 10-day course of treatment), the "weakest" bacteria die. But not all of the infective bacteria are dead in the first few days. When we stop treatment after only five days, there are still bacteria remaining, and these bacteria are more resistant to our antibiotic. If these bacteria reproduce, they will most likely produce other bacteria that are more resistant.

The evolution of bacteria is also sped up by their ability to trade small pieces of DNA with each other. Often, these pieces of DNA contain genes that allow the bacteria to produce proteins that help them to resist the very chemicals that we use to kill them.

II

Physical
Science

Chapter 5:
Structure of Matter

Introduction

What is matter? A good definition provides examples rather than just phrases to be memorized. Matter has mass and volume and occupies space. This describes almost everything in your immediate surroundings. The exceptions—that is, "things" that are not matter—are forms of energy. The light that falls on the pages of this book is energy. The heat produced by the combustion of the gas from your stove to boil the potatoes for supper is energy. If it is not matter, then it is energy. What is the nature of the matter around us? The diagram in Figure 5-1 is one way in which chemists classify matter:

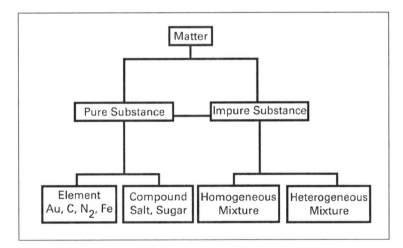

Figure 5-1. Classification of matter.

Mixtures

A **mixture** is a combination of two or more substances in which the substances retain their distinct identities. Different mixtures can have different compositions; for example, two solutions of sugar water can have different compositions. However, as long as the mixture has a constant composition throughout, it is classified as **homogeneous**. Examples of homogeneous mixtures include stainless steel, bronze, brass (all alloys of metals), salt or sugar dissolved in water, and the major gaseous components that make up the atmosphere: nitrogen, oxygen, and carbon dioxide. If a mixture has a variable composition, depending on where it is sampled, then it is a **heterogeneous** mixture. Examples of heterogeneous mixtures include chocolate chip ice cream; Italian or blue cheese salad dressing; many rocks; and simple mechanical mixtures of soil, sand, and pebbles. Mixtures, both homogeneous and heterogeneous, can be separated into their original substances, usually by simple means based on the physical and chemical properties of the component parts. However, homogeneous mixtures, which chemists call solutions, cannot be separated by simple filtration. Pure substances, as opposed to mixtures, are either elements, a type of matter composed of the same type of atoms (e.g., gold, carbon, iron, copper), or compounds that are composed of two or more different kinds of atoms held together by chemical bonds.

Mass

All matter has **mass**, which is a measure of the quantity of matter present. The **weight** of a piece of matter is due to the gravitational attraction for the mass of matter by Earth and can vary, depending on where the matter is located. **Volume** is a property of matter that is the amount of space an object occupies. When we compare the amount of mass with the volume of an object, we can determine the density of an object. The **density** of an object is the ratio of its mass to its volume. In more familiar terms:

$$D = \frac{m}{V}$$

where D is density, m is mass, and V is the volume of the object.

All matter—everything that has mass and volume—is composed of atoms. Atoms are the "building blocks" of matter. To date we know of 112 different atoms. These atoms are collectively known as the **chemical elements**. Only 88 elements are found in nature: some in their pure state and others in combination with other elements (see the section on Chemical Bonding). Other elements (e.g., americium, californium, einsteinium) are not found in nature but are made in laboratories using high-energy particle accelerators and nuclear reactors.

Hydrogen, the simplest atom, makes up more than 90% of all the matter in the universe. Elements "heavier" than hydrogen are made in the interior of stars and are dispersed into interstellar space by the explosion of stars when they "die." Most elements in our surroundings are the result of stellar explosions that occurred prior to the "birth" of our solar system. Very few of the elements are common to life on Earth. These are carbon, hydrogen, nitrogen, and oxygen, and a few others that present in trace amounts.

In our discussion, atom and element are used interchangeably and refer to the smallest part that identifies the type of matter we are considering. Atoms of each element, however, are different. To understand this concept, we need to look at the structure of atoms.

Structure of Atoms

Even though we say atoms are the "building blocks" of matter, understanding their structure is important to understanding how matter undergoes change. All atoms are composed of three basic particles; electrons, protons, and neutrons. **Protons** and **neutrons** (collectively called **nucleons**) reside in the central region of the atom known as the **nucleus**. Two kinds of charge are associated with the particles of matter, negative and positive. The proton and neutron are very nearly equal in mass. However, the proton is positively charged, whereas the neutron has no charge. The **electrons**, having a negative charge equal in magnitude (size) to the positive charge of the proton, surround the nucleus like bees in a hive. The electrons, however, are very small, roughly 1/1850 the mass of a proton; in other words, 1850 electrons are needed to equal the mass of 1 proton. The mass of atoms, and by extension, matter, is primarily due to the densely packed nucleus of protons and neutrons. Most of the mass (nearly 100%) is located in a space (volume) that represents about 1/10,000 that of the entire atom's volume. This is summarized in the table below.

Particle	Relative Mass (amu)	Charge	Location
Proton	1	+1	Nucleus
Neutron	1	0	Nucleus
Electron	1/1850	-1	Electron "cloud"

Physicists continue to do research on the particulate nature of matter. While we know that protons and neutrons are made up of still smaller particles called quarks (the electron is not), it will not be necessary for us to view matter at this level of fineness or complexity.

These three particles in combination account for all the known elements in the universe. What particle then gives gold its "goldness," silver its "silverness," or carbon its "carboness"? The answer is the number of protons that an atom has in its nucleus. Scientists use the term **atomic number** to refer to the number of protons in an atom's nucleus. Gold is the element gold because it has 79 protons in its nucleus, while silver is the element silver because it has 47 protons in its nucleus, and carbon is the element carbon because it has 6 protons in its nucleus. *Definition: Atomic number is the number of protons present in the nucleus of an atom.* On the periodic table of the elements the atomic number usually appears above the symbol for the element, is always an integer and never a decimal number, and determines the order that each element appears in the table.

Along with atomic number, scientists use the term **mass number** to count or keep track of the total number of particles in the nucleus; that is, how many protons and neutrons an element has. The mass number is also always an integer number. *Definition: Mass number is the number of protons and neutrons present in the nucleus of an element. This is always an integer greater than or equal to one*

Scientists use the following notation to summarize these terms and what they represent: "X" or some other variable represents the symbol for any element. The atomic number is shown in the subscript while the mass number is shown in the superscript. Some examples will help illustrate these notations and why atoms of different elements are not identical to each other.

Example 1: ^1_1H Example 2: ^2_1H Example 3: ^3_1H

A few questions will help guide us through the meaning of these examples. How many protons does each example have? How many neutrons does each example have? How many electrons does each example have? And finally, what is the name or chemical identity of each example?

Isotopes

The previous three examples all have the same atomic number and are, therefore, the same element, hydrogen. The number of protons in the nucleus of an element tells us which element we have. Hydrogen, for example, always has a single proton in the nucleus. Helium has two protons in its nucleus, while any atom with six protons is carbon. What is different in the above examples is the number of neutrons. Atoms of the same element may have a different number of neutrons. Thus, these variations of the same element are called **isotopes**. *Definition: Isotopes are forms of the same element with the same number of protons but a different number of neutrons.*

Isotopes are distinguished from one another by using the element name followed by the mass number of the specific isotope. The special nature of hydrogen as the first element and the most abundant element in the universe has been recognized by naming the three isotopes of hydrogen as protium (hydrogen-1), deuterium (hydrogen-2), and tritium (hydrogen-3) [Figure 5-2].

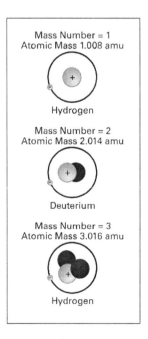

Figure 5-2. Diagrams for the three isotopes of hydrogen.

In fact, many isotopes are radioactive. Most (99.985%) of naturally occurring hydrogen is protium, while the remainder is deuterium. Tritium is an artificial isotope produced in nuclear reactors. Nearly all naturally occurring elements have isotopes. Fluorine is a notable counterexample. Isotopes are useful in dating rocks and in tracing elements' paths. Let us summarize these ideas by creating a table:

Isotope No.	Mass No.	No. Protons	No. Neutrons	No. Electrons
Hydrogen-1	1	1	0	1
Hydrogen -2	2	1	1	1
Hydrogen-3	3	1	2	1

The atomic number (not shown) is the number of protons. For neutral atoms, the number of protons equals the number of electrons. The mass number is obtained by adding the protons and neutrons together. Note that the isotope name uses the mass number to designate which isotope of hydrogen is being identified.

An element's mass is a weighted average of its naturally occurring isotopes. Thus, the fractional (with decimals) mass is also reported on the periodic table. A weighted average is one that a teacher might employ to calculate your quarter grade in science, weighting each category differently as in:

Quarter grade = 5% of homework average + 30% of quiz average

+ 15% of report average + 50% of test average.

Chemists can determine the percentage of each naturally occurring isotope for an element by the use of specialized equipment and thus determine the average mass for all the naturally occurring elements.

CAPT Review Questions 1-4

1. Describe how you would separate a mixture that contains $\frac{1}{2}$ cup sugar and $\frac{1}{2}$ cup sand in a 2-liter bottle filled with water.

2. Identify the following examples as A, homogeneous mixture; B, heterogeneous mixture; C, element; or D, compound.

   Stainless steel   _____   Sweetened ice tea   _____
   Diamond   _____   Table sugar   _____
   Italian salad dressing _____   Pistachio ice cream   _____
   Air   _____   Water   _____

3. Describe the contents of the three boxes below as being elements, compounds, or mixtures, and explain your reasoning.

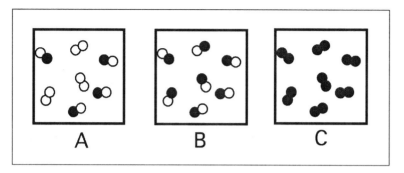

Figure 5-3. Accompanies Review Question 3

4. Fill in the table below.

Mass No.	Symbol for Element	No. Protons	Atomic No.	No. Neutrons	No. Electrons
16	O		8		
17	O		8		
18	O		8		

Answers to CAPT Review Questions 1-4

1. The difference in the physical properties of the components of mixtures is usually enough to guide us to a solution to the problem. Sand is not soluble in water, but sugar is. Filtering this mixture, say through a coffee filter, would leave the wet sand behind and the sugar water in a container below the filter. However, the sand is still wet with the sugar water so we would have to rinse the sand in the filter paper with several washings of tap or distilled water to remove any sugar that is still present. Left to dry, we can recover the sand from the mixture. How do we separate the sugar from the water? Heating the sugar water to evaporate the water is an obvious answer. However, we must be careful not to heat too quickly or at too high a temperature or the sugar will be burned; that is, we will change the sugar into water vapor and carbon.

2. Stainless steel is actually an alloy of iron and, therefore, a homogeneous mixture. Diamond is one of the rare and valuable forms of carbon atoms that are bonded together in a covalent network of atoms that give it particularly beautiful brilliance when cut properly; it is the hardest naturally occurring substance. Being of one kind of atom, it is an element. Air is a mixture of nitrogen, oxygen, and carbon dioxide. Traces of other gases exist to a smaller degree. When air is clean and unpolluted, it represents a homogeneous mixture. The components of sweetened tea are completely dissolved, making it a homogeneous mixture. Pistachio ice cream is an example of a heterogeneous mixture since the distinct parts to the

mixture—nuts and ice cream—are identifiable and not dissolved. Water is composed of hydrogen and oxygen chemically bonded to one another; therefore, it is a compound.

3. Container A has two different substances and is, therefore, a mixture; container B has a compound or a substance composed from different atoms; container C is an element since the atoms that make up the molecules are identical.

4.

Mass No.	Symbol for Element	No. Protons	Atomic No.	No. Neutrons	No. Electrons
16	O	8	8	8	8
17	O	8	8	9	8
18	O	8	8	10	8

The number of neutrons in any isotope is found by subtracting the **atomic number** (number of protons) from the **mass number** (the number of protons and neutrons). The first two columns in our table should be obvious, but how do we know the values to place in the spaces for the remainder of the table? The number of protons in the nucleus is by definition (see above) the atomic number. Therefore, by inspection of the notation of our three examples, we see that the atomic number for each is 8.

To calculate the number of neutrons for each of our three examples, remember that the definition of the mass number is the sum of the number of protons and the number of neutrons present. This is expressed symbolically below:

Mass number = number of protons + number of neutrons

Since the mass number and the atomic number (number of protons) are known, to calculate the number of neutrons, we subtract the atomic number from the mass number. For the first example, we have:

Mass number = number of protons + number of neutrons

16 = 8 + number of neutrons

Therefore, the number of neutrons is 8; this particular element has 8 protons and 8 neutrons in its nucleus. The table now looks like this

Mass No.	Symbol for Element	No. Protons	No. Neutrons	No. Electrons
16	O	8	8	8
17	O	8	9	8
18	O	8	10	8

Charged Atoms (Ions)

Atoms that contain the same number of protons and electrons are said to be electrically neutral; that is, they contain the same number of positive charges (protons) as they do negative charges (electrons). An atom's identity is determined by the number of protons in the nucleus. To become a **charged atom**, electrons, which surround the nucleus, are either "lost" or "gained."

Sodium is element number 11 in the periodic table. Recall that this means that the atomic number and, therefore, the number of protons and electrons in the neutral atom, is 11. Sodium forms a positive ion by giving away one of its electrons. Look at the following notations and determine why sodium is a positive ion in the second example shown.

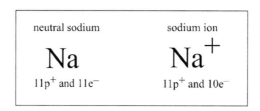

Note that since the number of protons has not changed, both atoms are the element sodium; the second example, however, has one less electron and is, therefore, carrying a net positive charge.

Chlorine, element number 17 (how many protons and electrons are present in the neutral atom?), on the other hand, tends to form negative ions by gaining electrons. Look at the following notations and determine why chlorine is a negative ion in the second example shown.

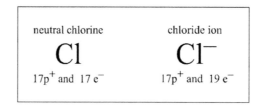

Note that since the number of protons has not changed, both atoms are the element chlorine; the second example, however, has one more electron and is, therefore, carrying a net negative charge.

Summary

The mass number of an element is often confused with the atomic mass of an element. The atomic mass is always a decimal number because it includes the mass of the electrons. The mass number is simply a count of the particles in the nucleus (protons and neutron) and, therefore, must be a whole number. Remember also that the atomic number is the number of protons in the nucleus.

CAPT Review Questions 5-18

5. In a neutral atom, the number of positive charges (protons) is equal to the number of negative charges (electrons). Therefore, if we know the number of protons and that we have neutral atoms, then the number of **electrons** will be the same as the number of **protons**.

Sample Isotope	Symbol for Element	No. Protons	No. Neutrons	No. Electrons
1	X	1	0	1
2	Y	1		1
3	Z	1		1

Complete your table by calculating the number of neutrons for examples 2 and 3.

6. An atom containing 9 protons, 10 neutrons, and 9 electrons has a mass number of
   a. 9
   b. 10
   c. 19
   d. 28

7. The smallest unit of an element that can exist either alone or in combination is the
   a. electron
   b. proton
   c. neutron
   d. atom

8. The nucleus of an atom has all of the following characteristics EXCEPT
   a. it is positively charged
   b. it contains protons and neutrons
   c. it has a volume that is much less than that of the entire atom
   d. it is very dense

9. The part of an atom that has an insignificant contribution to the overall mass of the atom is the
   a. nucleus
   b. electron
   c. proton
   d. neutron

10. Atoms are matter and, therefore, have mass and volume. Discuss the relevant contributions of the three particles of an atom—electrons, protons, and neutrons—to these two properties.

11. Complete the following table. Refer to the periodic table and provide the missing information (see the section Periodic Table—Organization, Properties, and Electronic Arrangement of the Elements).

Isotope Name	Symbol for Element	Atomic No.	No. Protons	No. Neutrons	Mass No.	No. Electrons
Chlorine-35						
Magnesium-24						
Chlorine-37						
		6			14	

12. The atomic mass of phosphorus is 30.974. This fractional mass is likely due to the existence of two or more phosphorus
   a. compounds
   b. isotopes
   c. isomers
   d. ions

13. Isotopes are atoms of the same element that have
   a. identical masses
   b. identical number of protons
   c. identical number of neutrons
   e. all of the above

14. An isotope of lithium contains 3 protons, 4 neutrons, and 3 electrons. Its atomic number is
   a. 3
   b. 4
   c. 7
   d. 10

15. Magnesium, atomic number 12 (12 protons), tends to form 2+ ions. Describe the differences between the neutral and charged atoms.

_____

_____

_____

_____

_____

16. An atom (or group of atoms) with an unbalanced charge is called
    a. an ion
    b. a positive ion
    c. a molecule
    d. a negative ion

17. In a neutral atom, the number of electrons is normally equal to the number of
    a. protons
    b. neutrons
    c. protons + neutrons
    d. protons - neutrons

18. Study the table below. Which represents an atom with a net negative charge?

Atom	No. Protons (Atomic No.)	No. Neutrons	No. Electrons
W	1	2	0
X	12	13	10
Y	31	39	30
Z	8	8	10

    a. W
    b. X
    c. Y
    d. Z

Answers to CAPT Review Questions 5-18

5. The different number of neutrons creates the different mass numbers of the different isotopes.

Sample Isotope	Symbol for Element	No. Protons	No. Neutrons	No. Electrons
1	X	1	0	1
2	Y	1	1	1
3	Z	1	2	1

6. **The correct answer is c.** An atom containing 9 protons, 10 neutrons, and 9 electrons has a mass number of 19.

7. **The correct answer is d.** The smallest unit of an element that can exist either alone or in combination is the atom.

8. **The correct answer is c.** The nucleus of an atom is positively charged, contains protons and neutrons, and is very dense. It does not have a volume that is much less than that of the entire atom.

9. **The correct answer is b.** Electrons contribute very little to the mass of an atom.

10. The protons and neutrons in the nucleus make up the majority of the mass. Electrons contribute very little to the mass. However, the electron cloud makes up most of the volume of the atom. To answer Question 10 successfully, you must know that an atom has two distinct regions, the nucleus and the electron cloud, and that protons are found in the nucleus and electrons, not surprisingly, in the electron cloud. A complete answer would include the following important ideas. The particles that contribute most to the atom's mass are the protons and the neutrons, which are located in the dense nucleus. Electrons, on the other hand, have negligible mass compared with protons but occupy a region of space around the nucleus that represents almost the entire volume of the atom. Though the nucleus represents only 1/10,000 of the atom's volume, it contains nearly all of the atom's mass.

11. **Filling in the blanks in this table requires recall of some basic facts regarding atomic structure. Remember the atomic number of an element is the number of protons in the nucleus. In a neutral atom, the number of protons and electrons are the same. How should you proceed to fill in the blanks? With the assistance of a periodic table, you can find the atomic number for each of the first three rows. The number after the isotope name is the mass number and as you may recall is the sum of the number of protons and neutrons in the nucleus. These few facts should allow you to determine the correct values for each blank in the table.**

Isotope Name	Symbol for Element	Atomic No.	No. Protons	No. Neutrons	Mass No.	No. Electrons
Chlorine-35	$^{35}_{17}Cl$	17	17	18	35	17
Magnesium-24	$^{24}_{12}Mg$	12	12	12	24	12
Chlorine-37	$^{37}_{17}Cl$	17	17	20	37	17
Carbon-14	$^{14}_{6}C$	6	6	8	16	6
Oxygen-16	$^{16}_{8}O$	8	8	8	16	8

12. **The correct answer is b.** Most of the elements have at least one or more isotopes. It is this mixture of atoms having a varying number of neutrons but the same number of protons that contributes to the atomic mass of the elements as a weighted average.

13. **The correct answer is b.** Remember that the number of protons identifies an element. However, the number of neutrons varies and affects the calculated atomic mass. The key words in the question are "same element," and therefore, the number of protons are the same for all isotopes of that element.

14. **The correct answer is a.** Atomic number is the number of protons. All isotopes of a particular element have the same number of protons. The first answer (3) is the number of protons in lithium nuclei.

15. Neutral magnesium (Mg, element 12) will have the same number of protons as electrons, that is, 12 of each. The 2+ ion will have two fewer electrons but the same number of protons as the neutral atom. Therefore, the notations for both are:

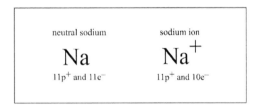

16. **The correct answer is a.** The key word in this question is **unbalanced** charge, while anion (negative ion) and cation (positive ion) are indeed examples of unbalanced charge, the question is not specific enough to choose either of these answers. A molecule is always electrically neutral; therefore, answer (a) is the best choice.

17. **The correct answer is a.** The only particles carrying electric charge are the electrons and protons. Their charges are equal but opposite. When the number of negatively charged electrons is the same as the number of positively charged protons the atom is neutral. If electrons are lost, the atom will be positive, and if they are gained, the atom will be negative.

18. The only pieces of information relevant to this question are the number of electrons and protons. Remember an atom becomes a negative ion by gaining electrons. A net negative charge indicates an atom with more electrons than protons present. The answer is Z.

States of Matter

Matter can be found in three states: solid liquid and gas (Figure 5-4). The speed of the molecules that make up the matter is different in each state. In solids, the molecules move very slowly, and because the structure of the solid is rigid, they remain in fixed positions in relation to one another. Liquids do not have as rigid a molecular structure as solids; while the molecules remain bonded to one another, they can move faster and with more freedom.

In a gas, the molecules are no longer bonded to one another; thus they move quickly and independently of one another. The "packing" of molecules also changes with state. The molecules in a solid are usually the most densely packed because they are bound so rigidly. A liquid is usually slightly less dense, because the bonds are not as strong. A gas is the least dense because the molecules are separated and can disperse into a large volume. A notable exception is water. Its solid form, ice, is less dense than its liquid form. This is because of the way water molecules bond; to achieve the rigid structure of ice, the molecules must actually be farther apart than in liquid water, where they flow around each other more easily. The addition or removal of heat causes a substance to change its state. Adding heat to liquid water, for instance, will cause it to boil and turn into steam (a gas). Some substances do not melt, but sublime, which means they change directly from a solid to a gas. An example is solid carbon dioxide, dry ice, which sublimes at room temperature.

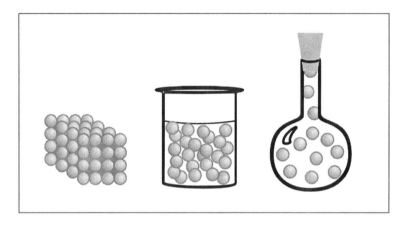

Figure 5-4. Three states of matter: solid, liquid, and gas.

Physical and Chemical Properties (and Changes)

Melting point, boiling point, solubility, hardness, density, and phase at room conditions are considered physical properties of a substance. Chemical properties refer to the tendency of a substance to transform when it reacts with other substances. For example, iron rusts, silver tarnishes, but gold does not tarnish in the presence of oxygen. Their different reactions reflect their different chemical properties.

When a substance undergoes physical changes, its chemical identity is unaltered. The phase changes of water (melting, freezing, boiling, condensing) are examples of physical changes. The water itself is unchanged whether it is in the form of ice or steam. Chemical changes, however, do alter the identity of the substance. The starting material or reactant is transformed after a chemical change. The product is a new arrangement of the same atoms into completely different substances from the reactants. Combustion or burning of a fuel, such as a log, results in ash, carbon dioxide gas, and water vapor. This is an example of a chemical change.

CAPT Review Question 20

20. See if you understand the ideas from above by trying the following examples:

One set of figures represents a physical change, while the other set represents a chemical change (Figures 5A and B). Describe which is which and why.

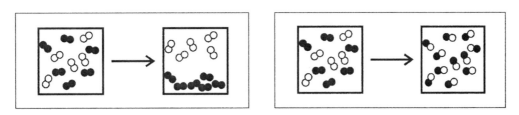

Figures 5-5. A and B. Chemical and physical changes.

Identify the following changes as either physical, P, or chemical, C

Grapes turn to wine	____	Wood burns to ashes	____
Water boils	____	Bananas and strawberries in a blender	____
An egg is fried	____	Grass grows	____
Film is developed	____	A car rusts	____

Answer to CAPT Review Question 20

20. Fermentation is a **chemical process** that converts the sugars of the grape into the alcohol of the wine. When anything changes phase, it has not changed identity; water boiling is a physical change. Cooking is always a chemical change, though it may not always look like chemical change has occurred. A fried egg is chemically different than a raw egg. In photography, chemical changes begin the minute the shutter snaps. Film is developed in varying chemical baths. Although the bananas and strawberries are mixed, nothing has changed chemically. A chemical change (photosynthesis) as well as a physical change (grass gets taller) occurs as grass grows; however, one should ascribe all of this to a chemical change. The steel (mostly elemental iron) of the car reacts in a moist environment to the oxygen in the air and forms iron oxide or rust, a chemical change.

Periodic Table—Organization, Properties, and Electronic Arrangement of the Elements

The periodic table of the elements organizes basic chemical information. The table is highly structured and contains a lot of information. It is important, however, to know how to read the table. Elements in the same column are members of the same family or group. These families or groups of elements share many similar chemical and physical properties that allow chemists to make predictions about their behaviors in chemical situations. These traits vary predictably as one moves across the periodic table along a row, also known as a series or period of elements. *The chemical and physical properties of the elements are a function of their atomic number.* This is the "periodic law" and is the basis of the periodicity of the table. The elements are arranged in an increasing order of atomic number (number of protons or nuclear charge) and not according to increasing mass. A careful look at the periodic table will show a few inconsistencies of mass relationships, but the number of protons for any element is always one more than the element to its immediate left.

The electrons in the electron cloud are not distributed randomly but are found in a specific structure and arrangement. It is easiest to imagine this structure as analogous to the solar system. The atom's nucleus is like the sun, around which the electrons, like the planets, have distinct orbits. Certain numbers of electrons occupy each energy level or orbit. The electrons that are farthest from the nucleus and occupy the outermost level or orbit are called **valence** electrons. All elements in the same column in the periodic table have the same number of valence electrons. Because the number of valence electrons determines how an element will bond (you will learn more about this in subsequent sections), the elements in a family (column) will form the same kinds of ions and will bond in the same way.

The chemical reactivity of the elements is also a function of location on the periodic table. The most reactive metals, for instance, are on the left side of the table in the first two families (in addition to the familiar reactive metals such as iron (Fe) and copper (Cu) found in the center of the table), whereas the most reactive nonmetals such as oxygen (O_2), fluorine (F_2), and chlorine (Cl_2), are found in the upper right side of the table. The so-called "noble gases" are non-reactive and are found in the last column on the right side of the table.

As mentioned above, groups or families form the same kinds of ions because they have the same number of valence electrons. Atoms are the most stable (least reactive) if the outermost energy level is full. Therefore, if the valence electrons do not completely fill the highest energy level, the atom will either gain or lose the extra electrons so that the outermost energy level is complete and the atom is stable. For example, the elements in group I (also called the alkali metals) will always form a 1+ ion by losing their single outermost or valence electron. Elements of group II (also called the alkaline Earth metals) will always form a 2+ ion by losing two outermost electrons. Metals always form positive ions, or cations.

Nonmetal atoms, on the other hand, gain electrons to fill an incomplete valence level. By doing so, they become negative ions. Nitrogen and its nonmetal family members typically form 3- ions, whereas members of oxygen's family will form 2- ions, and those of fluorine's family (also called the halogens) will form 1- ions.

Periodic Table of the Elements

Key:

1
H
Hydrogen
1.00794

atomic number
symbol
name
atomic mass

A bracketed value denotes the mass of the longest-lived isotope

1	2	3	4	5	6	7	8	9	10	11	12	13	14	15	16	17	18
1 **H** Hydrogen 1.00794																	2 **He** Helium 4.0026
3 **Li** Lithium 6.941	4 **Be** Beryllium 9.01218											5 **B** Boron 10.811	6 **C** Carbon 12.011	7 **N** Nitrogen 14.0067	8 **O** Oxygen 15.9994	9 **F** Fluorine 18.9984	10 **Ne** Neon 20.1797
11 **Na** Sodium 22.99	12 **Mg** Magnesium 24.305											13 **Al** Aluminum 26.9815	14 **Si** Silicon 28.0855	15 **P** Phosphorus 30.9738	16 **S** Sulfur 32.066	17 **Cl** Chlorine 35.4527	18 **Ar** Argon 39.948
19 **K** Potassium 39.0983	20 **Ca** Calcium 40.078	21 **Sc** Scandium 44.9559	22 **Ti** Titanium 47.88	23 **V** Vanadium 50.9415	24 **Cr** Chromium 51.9961	25 **Mn** Manganese 54.9381	26 **Fe** Iron 55.847	27 **Co** Cobalt 58.9332	28 **Ni** Nickel 58.6934	29 **Cu** Copper 63.546	30 **Zn** Zinc 65.39	31 **Ga** Gallium 69.723	32 **Ge** Germanium 72.61	33 **As** Arsenic 74.9216	34 **Se** Selenium 78.96	35 **Br** Bromine 79.904	36 **Kr** Krypton 83.8
37 **Rb** Rubidium 85.4678	38 **Sr** Strontium 87.62	39 **Y** Yttrium 88.9059	40 **Zr** Zirconium 91.224	41 **Nb** Niobium 92.9064	42 **Mo** Molybdenum 95.94	43 **Tc** Technetium [97.9072]	44 **Ru** Ruthenium 101.07	45 **Rh** Rhodium 102.906	46 **Pd** Palladium 106.42	47 **Ag** Silver 107.868	48 **Cd** Cadmium 112.411	49 **In** Indium 114.818	50 **Sn** Tin 118.71	51 **Sb** Antimony 121.757	52 **Te** Tellurium 127.60	53 **I** Iodine 126.904	54 **Xe** Xenon 131.29
55 **Cs** Cesium 132.905	56 **Ba** Barium 137.327	71 **Lu** Lutetium 174.967	72 **Hf** Hafnium 178.49	73 **Ta** Tantalum 180.948	74 **W** Tungsten 183.84	75 **Re** Rhenium 186.207	76 **Os** Osmium 190.23	77 **Ir** Iridium 192.22	78 **Pt** Platinum 195.08	79 **Au** Gold 196.967	80 **Hg** Mercury 200.59	81 **Tl** Thallium 204.383	82 **Pb** Lead 207.2	83 **Bi** Bismuth 208.983	84 **Po** Polonium [208.9824]	85 **At** Astatine [209.9871]	86 **Rn** Radon [222.0176]
87 **Fr** Francium [223.0197]	88 **Ra** Radium [226.0254]	103 **Lr** Lawrencium [262.1098]	104 **Rf** Rutherfordium [261.1089]	105 **Ha** Hahnium [262.1144]	106 **Sg** Seaborgium [263.1186]	107 **Ns** Nielsbohrium [262.1231]	108 **Hs** Hassium [265.1306]	109 **Mt** Meitnerium [266.1378]	110 [269.1]	111 [272.1]	112 [277.1]						

Lanthanides

57	58	59	60	61	62	63	64	65	66	67	68	69	70
La Lanthanum 138.906	**Ce** Cerium 140.115	**Pr** Praseodymium 140.908	**Nd** Neodymium 144.24	**Pm** Promethium [144.9127]	**Sm** Samarium 150.36	**Eu** Europium 151.965	**Gd** Gadolinium 157.25	**Tb** Terbium 158.925	**Dy** Dysprosium 162.5	**Ho** Holmium 164.93	**Er** Erbium 167.26	**Tm** Thulium 168.934	**Yb** Ytterbium 173.04

Actinides

89	90	91	92	93	94	95	96	97	98	99	100	101	102
Ac Actinium [227.0278]	**Th** Thorium 232.0381	**Pa** Protactinium 231.06588	**U** Uranium 238.0289	**Np** Neptunium [237.0482]	**Pu** Plutonium [244.0642]	**Am** Americium [243.0614]	**Cm** Curium [247.0703]	**Bk** Berkelium [247.0703]	**Cf** Californium [251.0796]	**Es** Einsteinium [252.0830]	**Fm** Fermium [257.0951]	**Md** Mendelevium [258.0984]	**No** Nobelium [259.1011]

The noble gases only react in rare instances under extreme conditions of temperature or pressure. Their highest level of electrons is already complete. Having eight outermost electrons seems to be a very stable configuration for atoms. By forming ions, positive or negative, atoms achieve the "octet" of valence electrons that the noble gases have. This is part of the rule of octets, discussed later in the section on Chemical Bonding. The common positive and negative ions for some of the elements are shown in Figure 5-6:

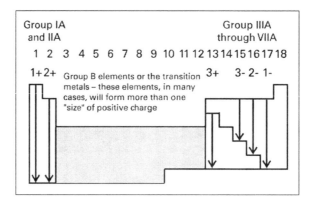

Figure 5-6. Common positive and negative ions for some of the elements.

The periodic table above summarizes some of the common ions formed by the representative elements or the so-called **Group A** elements (columns 1, 2, 13–17). Try the following:

Question: How many valence or outermost electrons do elements in Group 13 have?

    a. 13

    b. 3

    c. 2

    d. 1

Answer: (b) This is true because the units digit of the group number is 3.

Chemical Bonding

Chemical bonding is governed by electrical interactions between atoms. The three commonest bonds are, ionic, covalent, and metallic. **Metallic bonding** occurs, as its name would suggest, in pure metals and their alloys (a homogeneous mixture of two or more different metals), ionic bonding occurs between metal and nonmetal atoms, and **covalent bonding** occurs between nonmetal and nonmetal atoms. In **ionic bonds**, atoms give or receive electrons (forming ions) to complete their outermost energy levels, and in covalent bonds, atoms share electrons to complete their outermost energy levels. Each kind of bond will be discussed further in the subsequent sections.

Metallic Bonding

Metal atoms have loosely bound valence (outermost) electrons, which do not stay close to their original nuclei but become delocalized, and extend their orbits around the whole piece of metal. Because of this, metals are malleable and are good conductors of heat and electricity. Metals can be mixed easily, and the resultant alloys often have desirable characteristics, such as the strength and hardness of stainless steel (an alloy of iron, chromium, nickel, and a very small amount of a nonmetal, carbon). Metals form positive ions when they bond with nonmetal atoms (Figure 5-7).

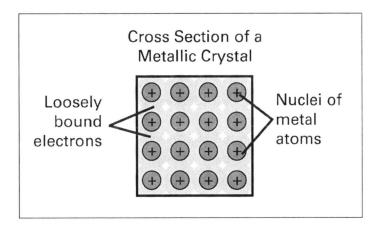

Figure 5-7. Formation of positive ions when metals bond with other nonmetal ions.

Ionic Bonding

Because metals lose electrons to become cations and nonmetals gain electrons to become anions, many compounds found in nature are formed when these opposite ions combine. These compounds are electrically neutral, because the opposing charges cancel each other out. Common examples of ionic compounds are ordinary table salt (NaCl), epsom salts, ($MgSO_4$), and the oxides of many metals such as iron rust (Fe_2O_3 and FeO) and aluminum oxide (Al_2O_3).

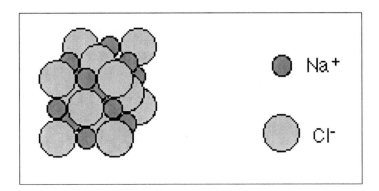

Figure 5-8. An example of an ionic compound, table salt

Chemical equations represent the reactions that form these compounds using the smallest number of atoms necessary to form a neutral compound. The crystalline structure of ionic compounds can be visualized as trillions of alternating positive and negative centers of charge.

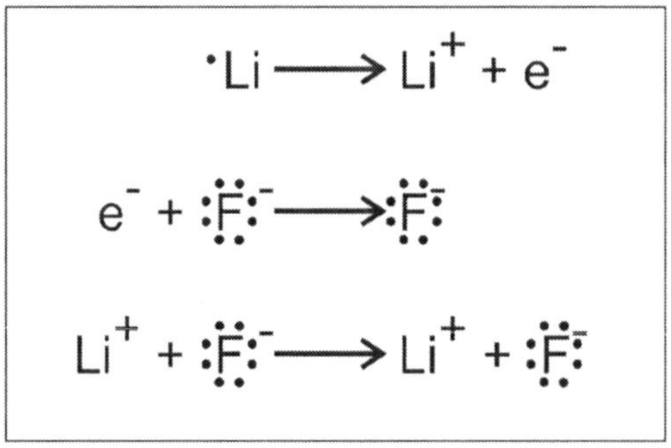

$$\cdot Li \longrightarrow Li^+ + e^-$$

$$e^- + :\ddot{\underset{..}{F}}:^- \longrightarrow :\ddot{\underset{..}{F}}:$$

$$Li^+ + :\ddot{\underset{..}{F}}:^- \longrightarrow Li^+ + :\ddot{\underset{..}{F}}:^-$$

Figure 5-9. An ionic bond with fluorine and lithium.

Ionic bonds result when metal atoms transfer valence electrons from their outermost energy levels to the nonmetal atoms' outermost energy levels. Both atoms now have complete outermost electron levels and are, therefore, stable.

Covalent Bonds

The third type of bond is the covalent bond in which atoms of nonmetals share their outermost electrons. Atoms typically share one, two, or three pairs of electrons to form the covalent bond.

Hydrogen, nitrogen, oxygen, fluorine, bromine, chlorine, and iodine do not exist in nature as unpaired atoms. They always occur as diatoms, or as two atoms covalently bonded to one another. The atoms share their electrons in the space between their nuclei so each atom completes its outermost energy level or have an octet (8) of electrons. This rule of octets works for many, but not all, covalent compounds and their bonding situations. Diatomic hydrogen (H_2) is a notable counterexample to the rule of octets, hydrogen molecules form by sharing a single pair of electrons.

Below is a diagram for the diatomic fluorine molecule (Figure 5-10). Note that each atom of fluorine has 7 valence electrons, but if it shares a pair of electrons, it has an octet or completed outer level. The electrons shown between the two symbols are the shared pair of electrons.

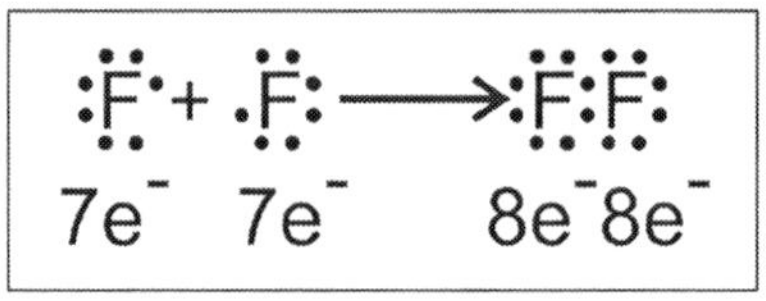

$$:\ddot{F}\cdot + \cdot\ddot{F}: \longrightarrow :\ddot{F}:\ddot{F}:$$
$$7e^- \quad 7e^- \qquad 8e^- 8e^-$$

Figure 5-10. The diatomic fluorine molecule is an example of a covalent bond.

Carbon chemistry

What is so special about carbon?

Carbon is the basis for all known living organisms, but why? The answer lies in the structure of an individual carbon atom, its resulting ability to bond in many ways, and its relative abundance on Earth. Carbon's atomic number is six, which means that any given carbon atom is identified by having six protons in its nucleus. A neutral atom of carbon also has six electrons, with two of these electrons rotating around the nucleus on the first shell of electrons. Carbon's second shell, which is able to hold eight electrons, houses the remaining four electrons. Since atoms with a less-than-full outer shell are unstable, carbon must find a way to obtain four more electrons to have a full outer shell. As a result, one carbon atom is able to make four separate covalent bonds by sharing electrons with other atoms.

This ability provides carbon with great versatility. Carbon can bond in single, double, and triple covalent bonds with other carbon atoms, and can also bond in various manners with oxygen, hydrogen, nitrogen, sulfur, and so on.

What are polymers?

Polymers are large molecules (macromolecules) made by bonding smaller repeating molecules, known as monomers, together in chains. These monomers are generally carbon-based molecules. For living organisms, the production of polymers serves as a method for storing larger quantities of molecules that may be needed later (for instance, animals are able to store large quantities of glucose by bonding individual glucose monomers together in branching chains to make the polymer glycogen). The use of polymers also serves as a method for storing and transmitting information (DNA, the genetic material of living organisms), and for serving various other functions (proteins, a polymer of amino acids, are used for transport, storage, building, and catalysis).

What are some ways that humans use polymers?

Many of the polymers manufactured for human use are the result of manufacturing processes that begin with the use of plant materials or fossil fuels. Early forms of rubber were manufactured exclusively by using the sap of rubber plants. While useful, this rubber had some properties that were not ideal. At high temperatures, natural rubber melts. This happens because natural rubber is made up of separate polymer chains that can move independently of each other. As such, natural rubber cannot be used in places where high temperatures are possible, such as in automobile tires.

In the mid 1800's, a man by the name of Charles Goodyear discovered, accidentally, that it is possible to alter the polymer in natural rubber. By mixing rubber with sulfur and heating, Goodyear found that it was possible to make a molecule that is far more elastic and able to withstand temperature changes. Why? The presence of the sulfur and the heat allow the individual polymer chains to form covalent bond bridges between polymer chains.

Scientists have often used this principle in chemical and biological research; that naturally-occurring molecules with some useful properties and others that are not ideal can be altered in ways that make the molecule more useful for our purposes.

CAPT Review Questions 21-37

21. Complete the following chemical equation regarding the formation of the water molecule from two hydrogen atoms and one oxygen atom (remember, oxygen will obey the octet rule, but not hydrogen):

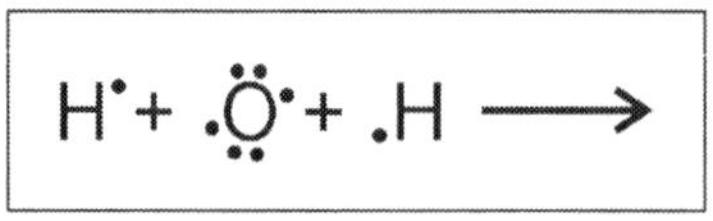

$$H^{\bullet} + \overset{\bullet\bullet}{.\overset{}{O}}{\overset{\bullet}{.}} + .H \longrightarrow$$

Figure 5-11. Accompanies Review Question 21

22. What happens to the "packing" of the molecules when ice turns into water or water turns into steam?

_____

_____

_____

23. Order the phases in increasing density (least dense phase to most dense phase) and explain your reasoning.

_____

_____

_____

24. Describe the freedom: of motion that the particles of each phase have. Think of the changes of phase as a short clip of a movie. How do the molecules move in each phase?

_____

_____

_____

25. Refer to the figure below. The drawing on the left shows a box containing particles in two phases. What phases are present? Suppose the particles are cooled to a very low temperature and draw what you think the particles would look like in the middle box. Now suppose the particles were heated and draw them in the leftmost box. Briefly describe your reasons for the drawings in the space below.

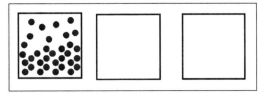

Figure 5-12: Accompanies Review Question 25

_____

_____

_____

26. All of the following are physical changes EXCEPT
   a. heating a platinum wire in a flame
   b. cutting paper
   c. boiling water
   d. tarnishing of silver

27. All of the following are chemical changes EXCEPT
   a. rusting of iron
   b. decaying of plants
   c. table salt formation
   d. melting of copper

Refer to this portion of the periodic table to answer the questions that follow.

Atomic #	3	4	5	6	7	8	9	10
Name	Lithium	Beryllium	Boron	Carbon	Nitrogen	Oxygen	Fluorine	Neon
Symbol	**Li**	**Be**	**B**	**C**	**N**	**O**	**F**	**Ne**
Atomic mass	6.939	9.01218	10.811	12.011	14.0067	15.9994	18.9984	20.183
Electron configuration	2,1	2,2	2,3	2,4	2,5	2,6	2,7	2,8

28. Elements that have similar chemical and physical properties are
   a. in the same period
   b. on opposite sides of the periodic table
   c. along diagonals from top left to bottom right of the periodic table
   d. in the same group

29. The mass number for the most common isotope of lithium is most likely
   a. 1
   b. 3
   c. 5
   d. 7

30. The number of electrons in an ion of fluorine is most likely
    a. 10
    b. 9
    c. 8
    d. 7

31. The element that is least likely to react with the others is
    a. boron
    b. neon
    c. carbon
    d. oxygen

32. The group number of the elements having a ⁻1 ion is Group
    a. 1 or (I)
    b. 2 or (II)
    c. 16 or (VI)
    d. 17 or (VII)

33. The periodic law states that the physical and chemical properties of the elements are periodic functions of their
    a. wavelength
    b. combining weights
    c. atomic masses
    d. atomic numbers

34. Nonmetals that are essentially without chemical reactivity are
    a. metalloids
    b. noble gases
    c. semiconductors
    d. gases like oxygen

35. The electrons that play an important part of an element's chemical properties are in
    a. the outermost energy level
    b. the middle energy levels
    c. a complete lowest energy level
    d. an incomplete lowest energy level

36. A horizontal row of elements in the periodic table is called a
    a. group
    b. series
    c. family
    d. octet.

37. Explain the different kinds of bonds.

_____

_____

_____

Answers to CAPT Review Questions 21-37

21.

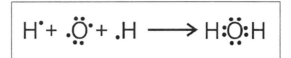

Figure 5-13. Accompanies Review Question 21

22. Particles in a solid are packed tightly, and connected by strong bonds. In a liquid, the most rigid bonds break but weaker bonds remain, and the "packing" is looser. When a liquid changes to a gas, all bonds are broken, and the molecules separate from one another completely.

23. The densest phase is the phase in which the same amount of matter occupies the least volume. Usually the gaseous phase is least dense, the liquid phase is denser, and the solid phase is the densest. Water is an exception. Ice, its solid phase, is less dense than liquid water. Note that ice cubes float in drinks, and icebergs float on the surface of the sea.

24. In a solid, the molecules are in fixed positions relative to one another, and "vibrate" around these fixed positions, much like the hub of a wheel moves around its axle. In a liquid, the bonds between the molecules are weaker, and the molecules slide past one another but remain connected. When a liquid becomes a gas, the weak bonds are broken and the molecules can move independently of one another. They move randomly to fill their container.

25. The substance in the leftmost box in the figure below is at its melting point, because the particles are partly in solid phase and partly in liquid phase. If the particles are cooled, they move more slowly, and eventually solidify, shown in the middle box. If the particles are heated, they move quickly and melt, forming a liquid, shown in the box on the right.

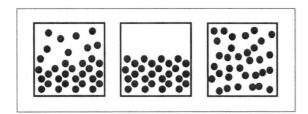

Figure 5-14. Accompanies Answer to Review Question 25

26. **The correct answer is d.** Warming a wire, cutting a piece of paper, and boiling water are all physical changes since the identity of the substance has not been altered. Silver tarnishing involves a chemical change

27. **The correct answer is d.** Rust, decay, and the formation of an ionic compound are the results of chemical changes. Melting, however, is only a change of phase and is, therefore, a physical change.

28. **The correct answer is d.** Groups or families of elements share chemical and physical properties. They are found in columns on the periodic table.

29. **The correct answer is d.** The weighted average of all the naturally occurring isotopes of lithium (Li) is 6.939, according to the chart. The most common isotope has a mass number close to this value, or 7.

30. **The correct answer is a.** The key word in the question is "ion." A neutral atom of fluorine has the same number of electrons as protons (9), but a fluorine anion gains an extra electron to fill its outermost energy level

31. **The correct answer is b.** Neon is a noble gas. It is very stable and hardly ever reacts. Its outermost energy level is complete, so it does not need to bond (react) to be stable.

32. **The correct answer is d**. Group 17, also called the halogen family, has an outermost energy level that lacks one electron to be complete. Thus, these elements gain one electron to complete their valence level.

33. **The correct answer is d.** The periodic table is arranged in order of increasing atomic number. Although it is also arranged according to increasing mass, there are some exceptions.

34. **The correct answer is b.** Noble gases are non-reactive because their outermost energy level is already complete.

35. **The correct answer is a.** Valence, or outermost, electrons determine the reactivity and chemical properties of an element. For instance, the missing electrons in oxygen's outermost energy level make it highly reactive. Oxygen is never found un-bonded in nature. By contrast the complete valence level of the noble gases makes them very stable and non-reactive.

36. **The correct answer is b.** Remember that a column is called a family or a group.

37. Metallic bonds occur between metals. Although electrons are not shared, they become delocalized from their original nuclei and flow around the entire piece of metal. Ionic bonds are formed between metals and nonmetals. Electrons are lost or

gained by the reactants. Covalent bonds are formed between nonmetals. Pairs of electrons are shared in order to fill the valence levels of both atoms simultaneously.

Curriculum Embedded Performance Task

Strand II: Chemical Structures and Properties Laboratory
Polymers

Polyethylene, a plastic made from fossil fuels, has been modified by chemists to produce new polymers with different properties and behaviors. These new materials can then be tested to determine their behavior, which can then help to determine their possible uses. In this lab, you tested various types of plastic for their stress-strain behaviors, including:

tensile strength - the amount of pulling force placed upon a material before it breaks

abrasion resistance - toughness of material against scraping, scuffing or scarring

puncture resistance - ability of a material to keep moving objects from perforating the surface

As you consider this experiment, remember to think about the reasons that various materials are used for various purposes, and also the reasons that they are not used for other purposes. Also consider the following questions:

1. What is the independent variable? The dependent variable?
2. What type of graph would be appropriate for graphing the data obtained in this lab?
3. What can the shape of your graph tell you about the underlying variables being measured?
4. What features of this experiment are you able to control?
5. How are you able to control these features?
6. What features of this experiment are not able to be controlled? Why?
7. What results would you expect from this experiment, and what will these results tell you about your problem?
8. How valid is this experiment? Remember to consider how well the designed experiment measures the stated problem, the ability to control the experiment, the amount of data collected, and the reliability of the collected data.

Curriculum Embedded Performance Task

Strand II: Chemical Structures and Properties Science, Technology, and Society

Risks and Benefits of Plastic Products

In this embedded task, you were asked to use online resources to evaluate the usefulness of specific types of plastics in terms of both their risks and their benefits. Remember as you consider this task that the credibility of your sources is important. Just as you should always provide specific evidence to support an argument that you are making, the websites and articles that you reference should provide specific evidence to support their arguments.

Chapter 6:
Reactions and Interactions

Chemical Reactions

When **matter** undergoes a chemical change, the atoms of the starting material (**reactant**) are rearranged into new configurations through the breaking of old bonds and the forming of new ones. The new substance formed is called the **product**. A balanced chemical equation, which represents the chemical changes in a reaction, is a useful way for chemists to describe the reaction in a compact and informative manner. A balanced chemical equation correctly represents the following facts:

1. Atoms are conserved. The number and kind of atoms (i.e., **elements**) with which we start are the same as those that are present at the end of the reaction.
2. Mass is conserved, and energy is conserved. The total mass/energy content of the reactants is the same as the total mass/energy content of products.
3. Chemical formulas represent all numbers and elements present in the correct ratios. Water, for example, is always H_2O not HO or some other ratio. The correct formula, H_2O, represents factual information about the atoms in the compound. Water always has two atoms of hydrogen for every atom of oxygen.

Let's look at two statements of a chemical reaction and try to balance the reactions. Nitrogen reacts with oxygen to form nitrogen dioxide. The formulas for the reactants are N_2 and O_2, respectively (both are diatomic elements), and the formula for nitrogen dioxide is NO_2. So the reaction becomes in symbolic form:

$$N_2 + O_2 \rightarrow NO_2.$$

Notice the two reactants are separated by a "+" sign. This is read as "reacts with" and should never be confused with the arithmetic operation of addition. In this reaction, we can see that the number and elements on the reactant side (*left of the arrow*) is not the same as the number and elements on the product side (*right of the arrow*). This reaction is not balanced. In order to balance the reaction, we must use coefficients, or numbers placed in front of compounds to balance the reaction correctly. The following numbers are used:

$$\underline{}N_2 + \underline{2}O_2 \rightarrow \underline{2}NO_2$$

N_2 means simply two atoms of nitrogen (N) and $2O_2$ means $O_2 + O_2$ or a total of four oxygen atoms. $2NO_2$ means $NO_2 + NO_2$ or a total of two nitrogen (N) atoms and four oxygen (O) atoms. The number of atoms of each element is now the same on both sides of the equation. The equation is now balanced. If the number of atoms of each element is balanced, then the mass is also balanced. To verify this, you must be able to determine the **formula mass of a compound**. To find a formula mass, you add all the atomic masses of the atoms present in the compound. The units of atomic masses can be any unit of mass. Therefore, we use a system of relative masses. An isotope of carbon is assigned a relative mass of exactly 12, and the masses of the other elements are compared to carbon. Hydrogen has approximately 1/12 the mass of carbon; if a given number of carbon atoms has a mass of 12 grams, then the same number of hydrogen atoms has a mass of 1 gram. Atomic masses are found on the periodic chart below the symbol for the element (see Periodic Table of the Elements, Chapter 5). Nitrogen is composed of two atoms of nitrogen in the reaction above. From the periodic table, we find that one nitrogen is approximately 14 grams, so two atoms would be 28 grams. Likewise one oxygen is 16 grams, so two would be 32 grams, and four would be 64 grams. On the product side, one NO_2 would have a mass of $14 + 2(16) = 46$ grams and $2NO_2$ (which means $NO_2 + NO_2$ or $2NO_2$) would then have a mass of 92 grams. Because the total mass on the reactant side, 28 grams (N_2) + 64 grams ($2O_2$) = 92 grams total, the mass of the reactants is the same as the mass of products. Consider the following examples:

Nitrogen (N_2) reacts with hydrogen (H_2) to produce ammonia (NH_3). As before, the arrow represents the reaction itself:

$$N_2 + H_2 \rightarrow NH_3,$$

which when balanced would be:

$$N_2 + \underline{3}H_2 \rightarrow \underline{2}NH_3.$$

The rearrangement of atoms in a chemical reaction usually involves a change in energy, which causes a change in the temperature of the surroundings. Burning a log in the fireplace releases heat energy to the surroundings. This is an example of an **exothermic reaction**, which releases energy and heats the surroundings. When an athlete uses a cold pack that involves the release of a chemical (ammonium nitrate) into water, the resulting reaction absorbs energy from the surroundings, and the athlete's ankle feels cold. When a chemical reaction cools its surroundings, it is said to be an **endothermic reaction**.

There are many varieties of chemical reactions. We will examine a few of these: combustion, composition or synthesis, decomposition, and neutralization reactions.

Combustion Reactions

Simple combustion involves the reaction between oxygen and another reactant, usually a hydrocarbon such as gasoline, wood, fuel oil, kerosene, or a candle. The products of complete combustion are always water and carbon dioxide. When incomplete combustion occurs, such as in the automobile engine, other gases besides oxygen are present such as NO_x, CO, and in some cases SO_x, (x in a subscript indicates that more than one formula for the oxides of nitrogen and sulphur exist) as well as molecular fragments of the original combustible material. Some examples of complete combustion reactions are:

Propane gas burns to produce carbon dioxide gas and water vapor, or symbolically:

$$C_3H_{8(g)} + O_{2(g)} \rightarrow CO_{2(g)} + H_2O_{(g)}.$$

Butane, which is a liquid under pressure but is a gas at normal pressures, burns to produce carbon dioxide gas and water vapor, or symbolically:

$$C_4H_{10(g)} + O_{2(g)} \rightarrow CO_{2(g)} + H_2O_{(g)}.$$

Neither of the above reactions is balanced. Try to balance the reactions as illustrated earlier.

Composition or Synthesis Reactions

In composition or synthesis reactions, a single new product is formed when two or more elements or compounds react. Earlier we looked at the following reaction,

$$N_{2(g)} + 3H_{2(g)} \rightarrow 2NH_{3(g)},$$

which involves elemental nitrogen gas and elemental hydrogen gas, reacting to produce ammonia gas. Yet another example involves the reaction between sulfur dioxide gas and water (liquid) to form sulfurous acid:

$$SO_{2(g)} + H_2O_{(l)} \rightarrow H_2SO_{3(aq)}$$

or

$$SO_{3(g)} + H_2O_{(l)} \rightarrow H_2SO_{4(aq)}$$

The above reactions are two of the main reactions in acid rain. Other reactions in the acid rain process are the production of sulfur and nitrogen oxides from the burning of fossil fuels and the combustion in a car engine. Many examples of this type of reaction take place in an aqueous (water) environment. The acid rain that is so much a part of the news worldwide is often one or both of these reactions along with a few others that involve the production of sulfur and nitrogen oxides from the burning of fossil fuels and automobile combustion engines. The subscripting being used, in addition to telling us how many atoms of each element are present in a compound, tell us the physical state of the reactant or product material.

Symbol	Meaning
(s)	Solid
(l)	Liquid
(g)	Gas
(aq)	Dissolved in water

Decomposition Reactions

In decomposition reactions, a single reactant is heated and breaks into simpler arrangements of elements or compounds. Some examples are:

Electrolysis (the splitting of water by electrical current):

$$2H_2O_{(l)} \rightarrow 2H_{2(g)} + O_{2(g)}.$$

Decomposition of carbonates by heating:

$$CaCO_{3(s)} \rightarrow CaO_{(s)} + CO_{2(g)}.$$

Neutralization Reactions

In neutralization reactions, an acid reacts with a base to produce a "salt" and water. A salt is a combination of a metal with a nonmetal (an ionic compound) [see the earlier section on Chemical Bonding:. The salt formed depends on the acid and base that react. A few examples will illustrate the nature of these reactions:

$$HCl_{(aq)} + NaOH_{(aq)} \rightarrow NaCl_{(aq)} + H_2O_{(l)}.$$

In this reaction, hydrochloric acid, (the same acid found in our stomachs) reacts with sodium hydroxide to form table salt and water. This reaction occurs in an aqueous environment, and the resulting solution is neutral, neither acidic nor basic, if exactly equal quantities of acid and base are mixed.

What exactly is an acid? What is a base? An acid is *any substance that when dissolved in water produce hydrogen ions.* Some examples follow:

$$HCl_{(g)} \rightarrow H^+_{(aq)} + Cl^-_{(aq)}$$

$$H_2SO_{4(l)} \rightarrow 2H^+_{(aq)} + SO_4^{2-}{}_{(aq)}$$

Bases, on the other hand, are *substances that when dissolved in produce hydroxide ions.* Some examples follow:

$$NaOH_{(s)} \rightarrow Na^+_{(aq)} OH_{(aq)} \qquad Ba(OH)_{2(s)} \rightarrow Ba^{2+}_{(aq)} + 2OH_{(aq)}$$

CAPT Review Questions 1-7

1. In an experiment, 32.0 grams of solid sulfur reacted with oxygen gas *to form* 64.0 grams of sulfur dioxide gas. How many *grams* of oxygen reacted with the sulfur?
   a. 16.0 grams
   b. 32.0 grams
   c. 48.0 grams
   d. 96.0 grams

2. A balanced chemical equation reflects the idea that the mass of the products is
   a. greater than the mass of the reactants.
   b. less than the mass of the reactants.
   c. equal to the mass of the reactants.
   d. not related to the mass of the reactant.

3. When steel wool rusts, the iron in the steel wool combines with
   a. nitrogen.
   b. carbon dioxide.
   c. oxygen.
   d. hydrogen.

4. Which of the following statements best describes the energy transformation that occurs when a piece of paper burns?
   a. Mechanical energy changes to chemical energy.
   b. Chemical energy changes to heat and light energy.
   c. Heat energy and light energy change to chemical energy.
   d. Mechanical energy changes to heat and light energy.

5. A rolled newspaper log was burned in a fireplace. Which statement is true about the leftover ashes when they are compared to the original unburned newspaper?

   a. The ashes have less chemical energy than the unburned newspaper.

   b. The ashes have more mechanical energy than the unburned newspaper.

   c. The ashes occupy the same amount of space as the unburned newspaper.

   d. The ashes have the same molecular structure as the unburned newspaper.

6. Which of the following equations best represents the burning of a newspaper?

   a. Newspaper + $CO_2 \rightarrow O_2 + H_2O$ + energy

   b. Newspaper + $O_2 \rightarrow CO_2 + H_2O$ + energy

   c. Newspaper + $H_2O \rightarrow O_2 + CO_2$ + energy

   d. Newspaper $\rightarrow CO_2 + O_2 + H_2O$ + energy

7. A sample of lake water in the northeast part of New York State has a pH of 6.5. Which explanation of this pH is _most_ reasonable?

   a. The slightly basic pH represents clean air.

   b. The slightly acidic pH represents clean air.

   c. The acidic pH indicates that a pollution source must be upwind.

   d. The basic pH indicates that a pollution source must be upwind.

Answers to CAPT Review Answers 1-7

1. **The correct answer is b.** The key word in this question is grams. The actual mass of oxygen, or even its relative mass, is not important. Recall that mass is conserved in a chemical reaction. The total mass of the reactants must be the same as the total mass of products. So we might write the following expression to represent this fact:

$$32.0 \text{ grams sulfur} + X \text{ grams oxygen} = 64.0 \text{ sulfur dioxide.}$$

Solving for "X" gives

$$X \text{ grams oxygen} = 64.0 \text{ sulfur dioxide} - 32.0 \text{ grams sulfur} = 32.0 \text{ grams of oxygen.}$$

You should also note the possible wrong answers that you might conceivably calculate: mass of oxygen atoms alone (16.0 grams), the mass of sulfur dioxide and oxygen atoms alone, (48.0 grams), the mass of the reactant, sulfur (32.0 grams), and the mass of the product, sulfur dioxide (64.0 grams).

Remember that a chemical reaction is divided into two parts, the **reactants** and the **products**. Usually, we can tell which is which by looking for the phrase in bold letters above (**to form**) or some of the alternative phrases such as "to produce" or "to yield." These phrases separate the reactants from the products. The actual balanced equation for this reaction would look like this:

$$S_{(s)} + O_{2(g)} \rightarrow SO_{2(g)}$$

In order to conserve mass in this reaction, there must be 32 grams of oxygen. This is the law of conservation of mass.

2. **The correct answer is c.** A balanced chemical equation reflects the idea that the mass of the products is equal to the mass of the reactants.

3. **The correct answer is c.** The first three answers listed represent the major gaseous components of our atmosphere. Oxygen is the most reactive gas of the three listed. Consequently, in a moist environment, it naturally combines with many metals, including iron.

4. **The correct answer is b.** A piece of paper has energy stored in the bonds of the molecules that make it up. When the paper is burned, the bonds are broken and the energy is released as heat and light (flames). The transformation of chemical energy into heat, light, and even sound is characteristic of many chemical changes.

5. **The correct answer is c.** Chemical energy is energy "stored" due to the position of atoms in a compound's structure. When the paper (a wood by-product) combusts, a chemical change occurs, which results in the formation of partially combusted products, such as ash, some gases, heat, and light. The ashes have less chemical energy than the unburned newspaper since an exothermic reaction releasing energy to the surroundings has occurred.

6. **The correct answer is b.** Combustion, or burning of newspaper, always involves oxygen as a reactant. One way to put a fire out is to deprive it of oxygen. Oxygen, itself, does not burn. It supports or is required for combustion or burning; it is the paper (the fuel) that burns.

7. **The correct answer is b.** The pH scale has values ranging from 1 to 14. Values lower than 7 are acid, and values greater than 7 are basic. Clean rain or snow has a pH of 6.5 because of naturally forming carbonic acid. Only if the pH is 3-5 is precipitation considered dangerously acidic. Answer (b) is the only correct choice.

Chapter 7:
Electricity and Magnetism

Electricity and Magnetism

All matter contains three fundamental particles, electrons, protons, and neutrons. The electron and its properties have successfully accounted for our understanding of the chemical as well as the physical properties of matter. The properties of electricity and magnetism were first described by the ancients, but not until the Scottish physicist, James Clerk Maxwell, were the two forces of electricity and magnetism defined in a mathematical theory that led to greater insight and understanding of these two separate but related forces. A review of the three fundamental particles will help us understand electricity and magnetism.

Electricity is the application of charges in motion. A simple electric circuit makes use of the stored chemical energy of a battery, direct current, (DC) or the outlet of our homes connected to our local power plant, alternating current (AC). An external circuit is the path through which electrons can move and do work for us such as light a bulb, run a toy car or power our CD players. This process of using a flow of electrons to due work was first studied in a practical manner by such scientists as Michael Faraday, Georg Simon Ohm, Alessandro Volta, André Ampère, Nikola Tesla and Thomas Edison, to name a few.

An older and a simpler form of the idea of electricity originated with the Greeks when they discovered that pieces of amber (fossilized tree resin (sap)) when rubbed would attract other bits of matter. We call this "static electricity". We are aware of this today if we shuffle across a rug on a dry day and then bring our finger near to a metal object, such as a door knob or window frame, and a spark of electricity "zaps" across the narrow gap between our finger and the object. A balloon when rubbed vigorously on a sweater or our heads will apparently "stick" to the wall because we have created a charge on the surface of the balloon that is said to be static. This charged balloon will cause the "particles" of the wall to be attracted by inducing the opposite kind of charges to be near the surface of the wall. (Remember opposites attract).

Magnetism has been known since ancient times when it was first noticed that certain rocks (loadstone) attracted certain metals such as iron. Today we know that magnetism in such metals as cobalt, nickel, and iron is due the particular alignment of the electron spins in the atoms of these metals. Like electric charge, magnets can both repel or attract each other. Unlike electricity, magnets always have two poles, N(orth) and S(outh). If you break a magnet it will still have two poles, N and S. Electric charge, on the other hand, can exist alone or separated. Magnetism can be induced in a ferromagnetic material (such as cobalt, nickel and iron) by an electric current. Wrapping a nail with a copper wire attached to a source of electricity, such as a battery, will induce or cause the nail to exhibit a magnetic field (an electromagnet). In a similar fashion a magnet that is moved rapidly in and out of a coil of wire will in turn cause a movement of electrons in the coil of wire and hence produce an electric current. This is the basis of the conversion of the heat from nuclear or coal fired power plants or the motion of water cascading through the structure of a dam to electricity via a generator.

CAPT Review Questions 1-3

1. A balloon is rubbed with a piece of cloth. As a result, the balloon has a negative charge. Which of the following statement explains how this happened?
   a. Electrons have moved from the inside to the outside of the balloon.
   b. Positive charges have traveled from the balloon to the cloth.
   c. Electrons have moved from the balloon to the cloth.
   d. Electrons have traveled from the cloth to the balloon.

2. Static electricity happens when electrons pass from one object to another, such as from your hair to a comb as you comb your hair. If you then hold the comb near small pieces of paper, then some of the bits of paper will jump toward the comb and appear to "hang" in midair. The bits of paper and the comb
   a. attract each other because they have the same charges
   b. attract each other because they have opposite charges
   c. repel each other because they have the same charges
   d. repel each other because they have opposite charges

3. Your sister rubs a balloon on her hair for several seconds and then, apparently defying the laws of nature, places it on the wall and it "sticks." Assume the balloon has become negatively charged. Explain why this happens.

Answers to CAPT Review Questions 1-3

1. **The correct answer is d.** Matter becomes charged by gaining or losing (transferring) electrons. Remember from the chemistry section of this booklet that you learned the protons, which carry the positive charge, are located in the nuclei of

atoms. The only answer that would make sense is for electrons to "travel" from the cloth to the balloon since the balloon has become negatively charged. Well what's wrong with the answer "Electrons have moved from the inside to the outside of the balloon," you might ask? If electrons move, then certainly this qualifies as a transfer of electrons. However, if electrons did move from the inside to the outside of a balloon, the total number of electrons (and protons) has not changed, and the balloon would be neutral or have no net charge rather than a net negative charge.

2. **The correct answer is b.** Opposites attract and likes repel. Two positively charged objects would repel each other as would two negatively charged objects. If bits of paper appear to move forward and "jump toward the comb," then they are attracted toward each other, and you must eliminate the responses that use the word repel. Opposites attract so the answer must be that the bits of paper and the comb attract each other because they have opposite charges.

3. In order for the balloon to "stick" to the wall, there must be an attraction of opposite charges. How did the wall become positively charged? This phenomena takes place because the net negative charge of the balloon induces the electrons of the matter in the wall to disperse or move away from the static charge of the balloon, thereby inducing the wall to have a more localized positive charge. This lasts as long as the balloon maintains a negative charge. The electrons will move due to moisture in the air or on the surface of the wall, and the balloon eventually loses its static charge and falls to the floor. Interestingly, this static attractive force can for a short time counteract the pull of gravity on the balloon!

Electric Current

Electric current is different in many respects from the problems we examined above because the electrons are in motion, not static or in place. Both, however still involve electrons. The motion or "flow" of charged particles, electrons in this case, in a conductor (usually a metal) is what we term loosely as electricity (more specifically an electric current). Several terms are used to describe this motion of electrons and are worth reviewing here. The *rate* (recall rate as described in the motion of objects like the bicycle and car in the examples above) of flow of electrons is measured in **amperes**. One ampere is the rate of flow of about 6.25 billion electrons through a cross section of a conductor in 1 second of time. The charge carried by that many electrons is called a **coulomb of charge**. Electrons "flow;" therefore, we have a current, only if there is a force to push the electrons. Water flows in a garden hose only if there is a difference in pressure between the two ends. This electrical force is known as **voltage**. Just as water encounters resistance to flow (friction between the walls and the water and fluid friction as the molecules move past each other) so do electrons encounter resistance to flow in circuits. This **electrical resistance** is measured in **ohms**. The relationship that exists between voltage, current, and resistance was first discovered by a German physicist, George

Simon Ohm. **Ohm's law**, as it is known, states that "the amount of current in a circuit is inversely proportional to the resistance of the circuit and directly proportional to voltage established across the circuit:"

$$\text{current} = \frac{\text{voltage}}{\text{resistance}}$$

or in units form

$$\text{amperes} = \frac{\text{volts}}{\text{ohms}}$$

Series Circuits

A simple **series circuit** is shown below. When the switch is shut, the circuit is complete, and electrons flow from the negative terminal of the battery through each of the devices in the circuit, one after another. The electrons do not "pile up" but simply move through the circuit to the positive pole of the battery, and the same current that flows through the circuit flows through the battery. If the circuit is open at any point (by a break in the conductor and open switch), then the current is interrupted, and none of the devices work.

Characteristics of series circuits can be described as follows. The electricity has but a single pathway through a series circuit. The total resistance in a series circuit is the sum of the resistance of each device connected in the circuit. In accordance with Ohm's law, the current in the circuit is found by dividing the voltage supplied by the source (the battery in Figure 7-6) by the total resistance of the circuit. The total voltage provided by the source is divided among the devices in the circuit. This is known as voltage drop across each device and is in accordance with Ohm's law; that is, the voltage drop across each device is directly proportional to the resistance of each device.

Parallel Circuits

A simple **parallel circuit** is shown below. When the switch is shut the circuit is complete and electrons flow from the negative terminal of the battery through each of the devices in the circuit. The electrons do not "pile-up" but simply move through the circuit to the positive pole of the battery. Unlike a series circuit, however, if the circuit is open at any point by a break in the conductor then the current continues to flow in alternate parallel pathways and the remainder of the devices will work. This is the manner in which our homes are wired. Some characteristics of a parallel circuit are:

- the more things you plug in to a parallel circuit the lower the total resistance becomes
- as the total resistance decreases, the total current increases
- plugging too many things in to one electrical outlet can create a fire hazard.

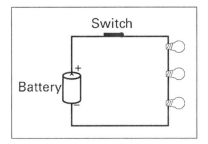
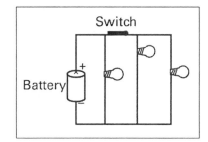

Figure 7-1A Characteristics of series circuits.   Figure 7-1B Characteristics of parallel circuits

CAPT Review Questions 4-7

4. To double the current through a resistor in a circuit, you must double the
   a. voltage across the resistor
   b. resistance of the resistor
   c. voltage across the resistor and double the resistance
   d. resistance and decrease the voltage across it by half

5. Using a multimeter to test the current and resistance of a variable resistor, the data collected were plotted as indicated on the graph below. The graph shows that current

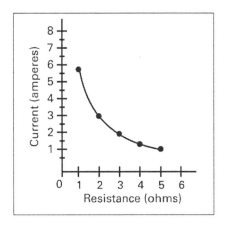

Figure 7-2

   a. increases when resistance decreases
   b. decreases when resistance decreases
   c. increases when resistance increases
   d. doubles when resistance increases

6. Lights used for decorative effects are not generally wired in series. Explain why.

7. What happens to the intensity of the lights in a series circuit if more lamps are added to the circuit?

Answers to CAPT Review Questions 13-16

4. **The correct answer d.** To double the current through a resistor in a circuit, you must double the resistance of the resistor. Current is directly proportional to voltage and inversely proportional to resistance. For the same resistance, if one wishes to double the current, all that needs to be done is to double the voltage. A direct relationship between current and voltage is precisely why this works. The inverse relationship between the current and the resistance means that if one were to double the resistance, the current would decrease by half. The answer that you must double the voltage across the resistor and double the resistance just leaves the current the same since one factor cancels the other.

5. **The correct answer is a.** This answer, of course, is the one that reflects the inverse relationship between current and resistance. The only answer that indicates this inverse relationship is that the current doubles when resistance decreases.

6. When wired in series, the loss of one device in the circuit will act like an open switch, and the entire circuit will be off, making it difficult to locate the "burned out" device

7. As you add more lamps to the circuit, the resistance increases, and the lights in the circuit will dim. In accordance with Ohm's law, the current will decrease (an inverse relationship), which dims the lights.

Chapter 8:
Energy Sources and Transformations

One of the fundamental relationships of physics is the law of the conservation of matter and energy. We believe with good reason and centuries of observations that matter and energy only undergo transformations from one form to another, and in the final analysis we can account for all the energy and matter with which that we started.

Simple Machines

Levers, pulleys, and inclined planes are some examples of simple machines. A machine, by definition, is any device that multiplies forces or simply changes the direction of an applied force. For simple machines, if we neglect the small amount of work lost due to friction then:

work input = work output.

Since work is force multiplied by distance (i.e., work is the force applied multiplied by the distance through which it acts), it can be said for simple machines:

input force × input distance = output force × output distance.

One of the simplest machines is a lever or so-called "pry bar." If the pivot point or "fulcrum" of a lever is placed close to the load one wishes to move or "lift," then a relatively **small force** acting through a **large distance** will exert a relatively **large force** to move an object through a **short distance**. A car jack works by this principle. Any machine that produces more output force does so at the expense of distance. Likewise, any machine that multiples distance does so at the expense of force. No machine can produce more work output than is input.

Properties of Sound

Sound can be described as wave phenomena. Sound, in order to be heard, needs a substance to vibrate and propagate its energy. Air is by far the most numerous medium (substance) present that allows sound energy to move from one point to the next. Sound energy is transmitted when something causes the air molecules to vibrate, that is, move in a way such that the molecules of the air are alternately compressing and expanding along a spherically enlarging dome centered on the source. These areas of compression and expansion are pressure waves. The molecules of air near the source, stay near the source, only the energy of the sound is transmitted via interactions with neighboring molecules. The **speed** with which sound moves is related to a number of factors, among them, the medium being vibrated (solid, liquid, gas), the density of the medium, which is often related to temperature and moisture content, especially for sound traveling through air. In air, at normal temperatures, sound travels at about 340 m/s. In water, sound travels at about 4 times the value of its movement in air and in a solid, such as steel, it travels about 15 times greater than in air. (Remember that cowboy holding his ear to the railroad tracks?)

The fact that we can talk about the speed of sound implies that there are other properties that we can associate with it such as the frequency, pitch, or wavelength. These three in particular are related mathematically as follows:

$$\text{Speed} = \text{frequency} \times \text{wavelength}$$

Water can serve as a more visual example for us in defining these terms. The **frequency** is simply the number of waves passing a reference point or the number of vibrations per unit time. The **wavelength** is the distance between like points along the wave's motion. For water this might be high point (crest of the wave) to high point or low point (trough of the wave) to low point. Frequency and wavelength of a wave are inversely proportional. Put another way, as the wavelength gets shorter, the frequency (or number of waves passing a reference point) increases. High-frequency sound waves are said to have a high **pitch**, while low-frequency sound waves are said to have a low pitch. The volume of a sound is related to the amplitude of the wave. The greater the amplitude of the sound wave, the greater the volume.

Properties of Light

Light traveling as a complex wave, unlike sound, does not need a medium to vibrate. What vibrates in a light wave are the electric and magnetic fields that are generated by the source of the light. Hence, the other name for this phenomena is electromagnetic (EM) radiation or simply EM radiation (more completely, the EM spectrum). Now the word radiation may cause you to flinch a bit. This is a word used by physicists to describe a mode of transmission, as in the heat radiates from the fireplace. The diagrams below illustrate the manner in which we view light as a wave phenomena and the entire EM spectrum (Figure 8-1).

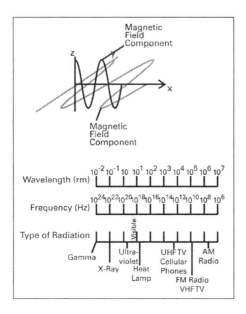

Figure 8-1. Light as a wave phenomena and the entire EM spectrum.

The smallest portion of the EM spectrum is, interestingly enough, the only portion of the spectrum to which our eyes are sensitive, the so-called visible light. The remainder of the EM spectrum is familiar to us in the form of such things as x-rays, radio waves, microwaves, and ultraviolet (UV) radiation. The energy of the waves is associated with the frequency of the wave. The higher the frequency, the greater the energy. So "light" with high frequencies — x-rays, gamma rays, and UV—have more damaging effects on humans than do low-frequency waves.

Sound and light can both reflect off "surfaces" and refract off "surfaces." Reflection of light is what allows us to see our image in the mirror, or if sound is reflected, perhaps an echo in a canyon can be heard. Refraction, on the other hand involves the **bending** of sound or light waves as they pass through mediums of differing properties, usually density. Indian tribes of the Amazon are aware of this bending of light waves when they aim their spears for fishing. The refraction and reflection of sound waves are used by technicians who use ultrasound (high-frequency sound waves) to examine an expecting mother and her baby.

When explaining color we can take advantage of the reflective property of light. All colors of visible light are "falling" on the surface of the grass. It absorbs all colors of the visible spectrum (thereby slightly warming the grass blade) and reflects the green back to our eyes. Green is reflected because of the pigment chlorophyll, which reacts with the incoming visible light in such a way as to reflect only the color green back to our eyes. The other chemicals in grass are either opaque to the light or absorb the light energy and become associated with the increase in temperature or motion of the grass "particles."

CAPT Review Questions 1-14

1. When operating, ordinary incandescent lightbulbs produce a lot of heat in addition to light. Fluorescent lightbulbs produce much less heat when operating. If you wanted to conserve electricity, which type of bulb should you use? Explain your answer.

2. Natural gas is burned in a power plant that produces electricity. In a house, miles away, a toaster is turned on. Describe the energy transformations involved.

3. What energy transformations and forces influence the battery-powered toy car pictured below? Explain your answer fully.

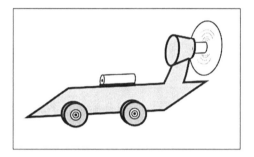

Figure 8-2. Accompanies Review Question 3

_____

_____

_____

4. Windmills are used to convert wind energy into a more useful form. In most cases, there are three steps in this process. The energy is in a different form at each step. Which of the following flow charts shows the most likely order of the energy changes?
   a. Wind energy → mechanical energy → solar energy
   b. Wind energy → thermal energy → mechanical energy
   c. Wind energy → solar energy → electrical energy
   d. Wind energy → mechanical energy → electrical energy

5. A bicycle is a composite of several simple machines. Describe where these simple machines are found on a bicycle: **lever** and **pulley**.

_____

_____

_____

6. Which of the following objects acts as a lever when pulling a nail?

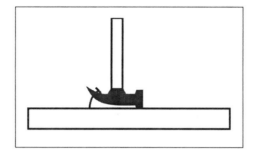

Figure 8-3. Accompanies Review Question 6

a. hammer
b. head of nail
c. board
d. point of nail

7. How does one make a loud sound, that is, one that has great volume?

8. Which bell has a higher pitch, a dinner bell or a church bell?

9. Do compression and expansion of air molecules travel in the same direction or opposite directions of each other?

10. Which of the following aspects of electromagnetic radiation best explains why electromagnetic radiation is both useful and harmful to humans?
a. Electromagnetic radiation travels at the speed of light.
b. Electromagnetic radiation travel through a vacuum.
c. Electromagnetic radiation is energy and can interact with matter.
d. Electromagnetic radiation is described in terms of both wavelength and frequency.

11. Why does the dental technician leave the room to operate the controls of the x-ray machine? Why not have operating controls in the same room?

12. My niece, Maya, wants to know why she can see herself in a mirror, but she can see through a window. How can I explain the differences between mirrors and windows?

13. Which of the following choices best explains why grass on a distant hillside appears green?
a. Grass reflects all colors except green.
b. Grass absorbs only green light from the sun.
c. Grass reflects green light more than any other color.
d. Grass transmits green light in the same way that green-colored cellophane does.

14. The setting sun often appears red. What is the best explanation for this?
    a. The surface temperature of the sun is lower at sunset than at other times of the day.
    b. Earth's atmosphere scatters blue light, so that at the Earth's surface mostly red light is visible at sunset.
    c. The path of light through the Earth's atmosphere is shorter at sunset than at noon.
    d. The surface of the Earth changes infrared radiation into red light.

Answers to CAPT Review Questions 1-14

1. The conversion of electrical energy into light energy is accomplished in two different manners in each type of light bulb. It is not necessary to know how each works but rather what each "produces." If an incandescent lamp produces heat (put your hand near a lamp that has been on for a few minutes and this will be obvious, but DON'T touch it, it **will** burn you) as well as light, then certainly some, maybe even a great deal, of energy is being transformed into heat and not light. The cooler fluorescent lamps (producing light by a different mechanism) can produce the same amount of illumination without the "loss" of energy in the form of heat. It, therefore, makes sense to conserve by switching to the more efficient fluorescent lamps.

2. The chemical energy released in the form of heat as natural gas is burned and is used to heat water to higher than the boiling point (under increased pressure). The steam generated is used to turn the turbines (giant fanlike blades attached to a shaft) of a generator. The shaft of the generator spins a coil of copper wire immersed in a magnetic field by the presence of large magnets near the coil to generate electricity. The electricity is provided via the power grid (transmission lines) to our home where it becomes available when we turn on the toaster switch to allow the electrons in the wiring to move. The electrons encounter a high resistance in the filament of the toaster and cause the filament to produce an orange-red glow. In addition, a large amount of the energy is transformed into heat, which we use to brown our bread or bagel to make toast.

3. The chemical energy "stored" in the batteries is transformed into electrical energy to cause the shaft of a small motor to spin and subsequently the mounted propeller to spin. Chemical → electrical → mechanical. The spinning propeller exerts a force on the air which counters with a third law force (for every force there is an equal and opposite force) on the car and the car moves forward. The other forces acting on the car are gravity and friction. The car is pulled down by gravity and the pushes on the Earth with a force equal to the weight of the car. The Earth pushes back with

an equal but opposite force. These forces are unrelated to the forward movement of the car with the exception of what frictional force results from the contact between the car and the surface upon which it rests. Since the car has wheels, the frictional force will be unbalanced with the force provided by the rotating propeller blades. The car will accelerate forward until the forces acting in the direction of the motion are once again in balance. The car will continue to move with a uniform speed until acted upon by some force to change its motion or the batteries die.

4. **The correct answer is d.** The four responses all start with the obvious energy source, wind. What follows this is what the wind itself accomplishes, making the blades of the windmill spin. The spinning of the windmill blades is a form of mechanical energy so the choice has been narrowed to either (a) or (d). The only useful choice and sensible choice after this is, of course, electrical energy, which is why we have windmills today. Of course 200 years ago, the windmill's mechanical energy was further exploited to pump water from wells or from low-lying countries such as the coastal regions of Denmark or to run a mill to produce ground corn to make flour.

5. Today's newer bicycles take advantage of the lever and pulley system to transfer the motion of our legs into the forward movement of the bicycle. The pedal (a lever arm), which is connected to the shaft of the front gear train (or pulley), allows the force we exert to be multiplied as we turn through many revolutions. The size difference of the combination of gear choices with two or three front gears (pulleys) as well as six to nine rear gears (pulleys) can make the largest hill child's play.

6. **The correct answer is a.** The handle of the hammer acts as a lever as it pivots on its head (the fulcrum) to extract the nail from a board.

7. The amount of energy expended is directly proportional to the volume or loudness of a sound wave. Striking the drum head with a small force creates a low volume. Clapping your hands in a "polite" fashion as opposed to slamming them together with great force makes the difference between a string quartet concert and a rock concert audience. The amplitude of a sound wave, then, is also associated with the energy used to generate the wave.

8. Frequencies of high vibrations are associated with small bells and, therefore, have a higher pitch. Pitch is our subjective interpretation of a sound's frequency. Of course, the church bell has vibrations of a low frequency and are, therefore, of a lower pitch.

9. The answer is in the same direction. Unlike water waves in which the particles are moving up and down while the energy of the wave is moving forward, sound energy moves from one point to the next because the particles of air are alternately

compressed and expanded. The vibration of the particles of air, or any material that can transmit sound, is in the same direction as the movement of the wave.

10. **The correct answer is c.** If matter and energy interact, and they do all the time, there is always the possibility of chemical change. The higher the energy interacting with matter, the greater the chance for change to occur. So keeping our doses of x-rays from the dentist's office to a minimum is important to our health and that of the technicians who work for the dentist.

11. The technicians who work in a dental or in an x-ray department are exposed to the x-rays on a daily basis, and because of this, they must take precautions to minimize their exposure to the x-rays. They also wear a badge, which is called a dosimeter to keep track of their level of exposure, which is carefully monitored to be sure they have not received overly high exposures to this type of radiation during the year. Your exposure, although cumulative over your lifetime, is not harmful if performed in the proper manner and is limited to small doses between longer periods of time than the dental technicians.

12. The same answer that explains why x-rays show bones well but not soft tissue, is what explains the behavior of visible light as it interacts with different materials. Visible light will "shine" through windows because windows are transparent to this type of radiation. Ultraviolet light, on the other hand, is nearly blocked by most glass and transparent plastics. Mirrors have a coating of either silver or aluminum on the rear surface to cause the light to be reflected. (By the way, x-rays will pass through soft tissue (soft tissue is transparent to x-rays to a large extent), but bones are said to be opaque to x-rays.

13. **The correct answer is c.** Grass transmits green light in the same way that green-colored cellophane does.

14. **The correct answer is b.** Although this is the correct answer, it is little more than a memorization of fact. Light that is not scattered is transmitted. Light of very high frequency, blues and violets, is scattered more. Conversely, light of low frequency, red, orange, and yellow, is least scattered and, therefore, better transmitted. During the morning and evening hours, the sunlight passes through a thick layer of the atmosphere, and as a result, the blues and violets are removed by scattering, allowing the reds to predominate. The sun always looks darker (more red) at dawn and dusk and more yellow at noon.

III

Earth
Science

Chapter 9:
Earth's Natural Resources

Essential Natural Resources

After reviewing this section, you should be able to answer the following questions:

What are natural resources?

Why must every nation import some natural resources?

What are renewable resources?

What is the carbon cycle?

What is the nitrogen cycle?

What are nonrenewable resources?

How can renewable resources become nonrenewable?

How can we make sure that natural resources will meet future needs?

What Are Natural Resources?

Nature provides us with the natural resources that we need to survive. The sun provides us with warmth and light. The Earth provides us with the oxygen for respiration; freshwater for hydration; soil for growing our food; lumber and rock for construction; and minerals for tools, electronics, and transportation. However, the Earth is a relatively small planet. It can naturally hold only so much life or so many resources. Until the last century, it seemed that we had unlimited fresh air, clean water, forests, farmland, fossil fuels, mineral resources, and a great untapped ocean. In 1900, the world's population was only 1.6 billion people. Today, there are over 6 billion of us. Now, we have come to realize the limited nature of the resources nature provides.

Why Must Every Nation Import Some Natural Resources?

Natural resources are not evenly distributed around the world. Coal is found only where there were enormous ancient swamps. The ores of most metals are found where mountains formed by the collision of tectonic plates. Wood is scarce in dry climates, and rich topsoil is rare in rain forests. The larger a nation is, the more likely it is to have resources. The United States and Russia both cover large portions of their continents and have access to a variety of resources. However, Russia has not been able to take advantage of many of its resources because the severe climate in much of the country makes construction and transportation difficult. The United States, with its temperate climate, has been able to build the railroads, mines, and foundries to take advantage of its extensive mineral and fossil fuel wealth. However, today we must import most of our oil and many important metals such as chromium and platinum. Today, no one nation has everything it needs to compete in the world's economy.

What Are Renewable Resources?

Natural resources are generally categorized as being either renewable or nonrenewable. **Renewable resources** are those that can be replaced through natural processes at a rate equal to or greater than they are being used. Sunlight represents the ultimate renewable resource. No matter how much solar energy you collect or use, there will be just as much available in the future. Such renewable resources are sometimes referred to as **perpetual resources.** Freshwater supplies are constantly renewed through rain and melting snow or ice. The oxygen and carbon dioxide in the air are constantly cycling through the biosphere, geosphere, and atmosphere. Life, such as trees and fish are also considered to be renewable resources.

Our air is the product of billions of years of geochemical and biochemical reactions. Four billion years ago, the air was toxic [i.e., composed of mostly carbon dioxide (CO_2), nitrogen (N_2), and water vapor (H_2O)] compared to today's atmosphere;. Today, the atmosphere's major gasses are nitrogen, oxygen (O_2), carbon dioxide, and water.

The major source of oxygen in our atmosphere is photosynthesis. In the presence of sunlight, the chlorophyll in plants combines carbon dioxide and water to produce glucose and oxygen:

$$6CO_2 + 6H_2O \xrightarrow{\text{In the presence of sunlight and chlorophyll}} C_6H_{12}O_6 + 6O_2$$

Animals and bacteria use the oxygen for respiration. The oxygen is absorbed during the decomposition of organic material and, in the process, generates carbon dioxide. This is then available for plant life.

What Is the Carbon Cycle?

In the carbon cycle, carbon dioxide is taken up by plants and through photosynthesis combines with water to create glucose. The plant uses the glucose as food for its own growth.

The carbon is stored in the tissues of the plant until it dies, and bacteria release carbon dioxide through the process of decomposition. Animals also release carbon dioxide in the process of respiration. Some carbon dioxide reacts with calcium in the sea water to make calcite ($CaCO_3$), which may precipitate out the sea water to create lime deposits. Also, a great deal of carbon is stored in fossil fuels—that is, in our coal and oil deposits. Most coal represents the remains of Paleozoic plants, and oil is from prehistoric phytoplankton. By burning fossil fuels, we release the carbon in the form of carbon dioxide back into the atmosphere. Likewise, by cutting down forests, we remove the growing trees' ability to store more carbon in their new growth wood. We know that increased levels of carbon dioxide may lead to increased global warming and potentially serious climatic changes to some of the world's major food-producing areas. Increased temperatures also expand the ocean's water, increasing sea levels.

The carbon and oxygen cycles are summarized in the following diagram (Figure 9-1).

What Is the Nitrogen Cycle?

The nitrogen cycle is a third important cycle involving our atmosphere. Nitrogen compounds are essential to biochemical reactions of living things; it is part of our DNA and proteins. It is an important component of plant fertilizers. Animals take up nitrogen through plants or the animals that eat the plants. The plants naturally take up nitrogen in the form of nitrates (NO_3^-), which are formed in the soil by some bacteria and plants. By burning fossil fuels, which contain nitrogen, we create nitric acid—a major contributor to acid rain. The acid rain may damage plants, may render lakes and streams too acidic for most life, and may rapidly leach important minerals from the soil.

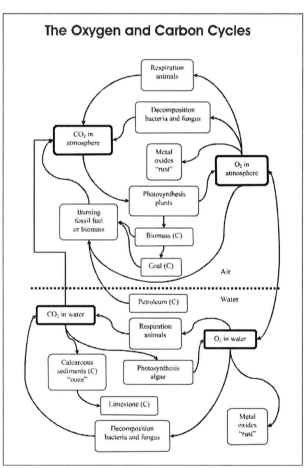

Figure 9-1. The oxygen and carbon cycles.

CAPT Review Questions

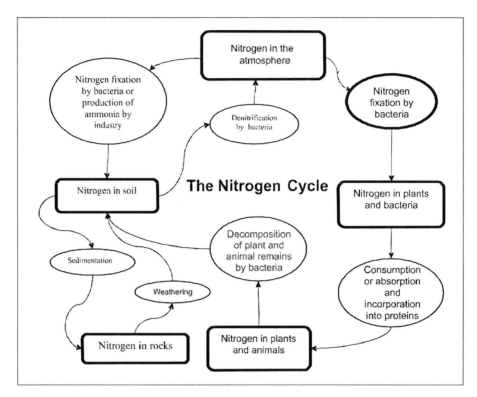

Figure 9-2. Accompanies Review Questions 1-2

1. The nitrogen cycle depends heavily on the work of
   a. plants
   b. animals
   c. bacteria
   d. geologic processes

2. Humans interfere in the nitrogen cycle by
   a. eating plants and animals
   b. mining nitrogen-bearing rocks and minerals
   c. killing nitrogen-fixing bacteria
   d. removing nitrogen from the atmosphere to make ammonia

Answers to CAPT Review Questions 1-2

1. **The correct answer is c.** Bacteria play a role in three to four parts of the nitrogen cycle. Plants play a role in only two parts of the nitrogen cycle. Animals play a role in only one part of the nitrogen cycle. Geologic processes play a role in only one part of the nitrogen cycle.

2. **The correct answer is d.** Humans extract large quantities of nitrogen from the atmosphere to make ammonia for industrial purposes. Eating plants and animals is natural part of the nitrogen cycle, not a form of interference. The mining of nitrogen-bearing rocks does not play a significant role in the cycle. Humans do not generally kill nitrogen-fixing bacteria.

What Are Nonrenewable Resources?

Nonrenewable resources are those that are being used at a greater rate than they are formed. Our fossil fuels and almost all our mineral and rock resources are nonrenewable. Most of the world's coal was formed in vast fern swamps over 300 million years ago. Most of our petroleum is derived from the oil found within the cells of the ancient marine phytoplankton. Most of our iron ore deposits formed hundreds of millions of years ago from slowly cooling magma bodies or by bacterial action in ancient seas. Building stone such as granite can be quarried only in certain areas. There is only a very limited amount of gold, silver, and platinum. As you read this, gold and silver deposits are forming in veins beneath the Andes Mountains, but because of their great depth and the high temperatures, it will be millions of years before they will become accessible.

How Can Renewable Resources Become Nonrenewable?

With increased demands, what may once have been a renewable resource may become extinct or no longer available. In the past, the lumber industry cut down trees faster than new trees grew. Now the industry is forced to look elsewhere for wood such as the rain forests of the Pacific Northwest and the Amazon basin. In the western United States, there is no longer enough water flowing through our rivers to meet the growing needs of agriculture, industry, residential development, recreational use, and environmental protection. Soil, is one of our most important natural resources. If properly managed, it is a renewable resource. If it is properly fertilized, organic material added, and care is taken to prevent erosion, soil can support crops indefinitely. However, if not properly managed, it becomes nonrenewable. In nature, topsoil is formed at rates of only centimeters per thousands of years. However, all over the world, soil is being washed and blown off the land. In dry areas, so much soil may be removed that the area no longer supports vegetation. The process of changing from productive soil to desert is called **desertification**. Today, this is extremely important in sub-Saharan Africa as overgrazed pastureland is being lost to an expanding Sahara desert.

Other important nonrenewable resources include bedrock, aggregates, ores, gemstones, and salt. The brown stone (arkose) quarried in Portland, Connecticut, was used in building town houses in many eastern cities and was even shipped to the West Coast. Granite was quarried along our coastline. Aggregates, river gravel, and glacial till are still dug up in open pit mines in many of our state's towns. Marble is quarried in western Connecticut to be ground into powder as the main ingredient in cement. Today, there are major quarries along the basaltic ridges, which run through the center of the state. These are the trap rock or basalt quarries, which contain the best stone to add to concrete and asphalt for making roads. In many areas, there are still rich deposits of minerals, but the high price of land, labor, and refining in Connecticut means that these minerals are no longer being mined.

How Can We Make Sure That
Natural Resources Will Meet Future Needs?

To make sure we have enough natural resources to meet our future needs, we need to practice both conservation and recycling. There is only so much oil to be refined into gasoline. The less fuel-efficient our cars are, the faster we are going to run out of oil. Even with our fairly high rainfall in Connecticut (1.12 m/yr), during dry summers, wells run dry, and some streams dry up. Recycling helps conserve natural resources by reusing what has already been refined. Aluminum costs much less to recycle from old aluminum cans than it does to refine the ore bauxite, the principal source of aluminum. People have been practicing recycling in some form since the dawn of history. Repairing instead of discarding can recycle most of a product.

Our population in Connecticut continues to grow. If we had to depend on just Connecticut for all our resources, as the Native Americans did 500 years ago (although even they traded for such rare materials in Connecticut such as flint for making arrow heads), we would be big trouble. There is not enough farmland to feed us. There is not enough copper or steel for buildings or transportation. There are no recoverable deposits of fossil fuels. Unless we conserve and recycle, we will run out of some of our nonrenewable resources and will no longer have the renewable resources that we need to maintain our present standard of living.

CAPT Review Questions 3-4

Below is a diagram showing the breakdown of renewable, nonrenewable, and perpetual resources.

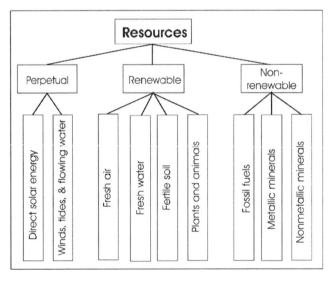

Figure 9-3. Accompanies Review Questions 3-4

3. The materials that make up a computer are largely
   a. perpetual
   b. renewable
   c. nonrenewable
   d. none of the above

4. It is important to recycle old computer parts because it
   a. allows us to buy new ones
   b. uses less energy
   c. conserves the resources used to make computers
   d. makes computers cheaper

Answers to CAPT Review Questions 3-4

3. **The correct answer is c.** Computers are made of nonrenewable resources, such as metals, plastics, which come from fossil fuels, and glass, which is a non-metallic resource. Direct solar energy, winds, tides, water, air, soil, plants, or animal products are not the materials used to make a computer.

4. **The correct answer is c.** The materials that make up a computer are available only in limited quantities. If we want to continue making computers, we have to recycle those materials. It is still possible to buy a computer even if you have not recycled your old one. The amount of energy a computer uses is not related to whether or not its parts were recycled. Recycling computer parts does not make them cheaper.

Freshwater

After reviewing this section, you should be able to answer the following questions:
What characteristics of water make it vital for life?
How does water affect the Earth's climate?
What makes water ice different from almost every other solid?
From where do we get our water?
If water is a renewable resource, how can we run out of it?
How do we manage our freshwater supplies?

What Characteristics of Water Make It Vital for Life?

Without water, there would never have been life on Earth. Water is the medium that carries nutrients and oxygen into and the waste products out of cells. It is the medium in which all biochemical reactions occur. Its bipolar molecular structure allows it to dissolve more minerals and nutrients than any other fluid. Water represents most of the mass of animal and plant cells.

Water's unique physical and chemical properties allow life to exist as we know it. The electrical charge of water molecules allows them to adhere to solid surfaces, resulting in the capillary action that allows water to work its way through plant tissue. Because water molecules have a positively charged oxygen atom on one side and two negatively charged hydrogen atoms on the other, they can wedge themselves into the crystalline structure of many inorganic and organic crystals and compounds. This action allows them to dissolve a wide range of minerals and nutrients, including waste products.

To be useful for living things, water must be in the liquid form. On Earth, with the exception of only the most extreme southern latitudes, water can be found in the liquid form. During the summer, even the Arctic Ocean near the North Pole may be free of ice. Nowhere on Earth (outside of the craters of active volcanoes) does the air temperature come close to water's boiling point.

How Does Water Affect the Earth's Climate?

Water has the ability to absorb and retain heat energy. The energy of the sunlight striking and penetrating the oceans is held and only slowly released. The currents of the world's oceans carry warm water toward the Polar regions and cooler water toward the Tropics. The transfer of heat energy is a major moderator of the Earth's climate, warming the temperature of some temperate zones and cooling others. The Gulf Stream carries tropical warmth toward Northern Europe. Cool currents such as the Labrador Current carry arctic water down along the coast of New England.

What Makes Water Ice Different from Almost Every Other Solid?

Water ice's unique crystalline structure makes it less dense than liquid water. As water freezes, the water molecules form hexagons, which take up more space than the individual water molecules of liquid water. As a result, when a water body freezes, the ice crystals float to the top, and water freezes over from the top down. Once the ice forms, it creates a barrier between the cold winter or polar air and denser, warmer water underneath. If water behaved as most other liquids do, which is to become denser as they crystallize, the ocean and lakes would freeze from the bottom up; eventually there would only be a thin veneer of liquid water on massive frozen oceans.

From Where Do We Get Our Water?

The water we have on Earth today is essentially the same water that has existed here for hundreds of millions of years. Earth's water is constantly going through the water cycle, which entails the processes of evaporation, condensation, and precipitation. In simple terms, water from lakes and oceans evaporates and condenses as clouds in the atmosphere. Precipitation forms, and it rains. The rain strikes the ground and runs into streams, which work their way to lakes or oceans, where the water evaporates again. The reality is much more complicated and will be covered in more detail in Chapter 10, Matter Cycling and Climate Change.

The World's Water

Location	Water Volume (km³)	Percentage of Total Water
Oceans (saltwater)	1,230,000,000	97.248
Glaciers (freshwater)	28,600,000	2.14
Groundwater (freshwater)	8,000,000	0.615
Lakes (freshwater)	123,000	0.009
Atmosphere (freshwater)	12,700	0.001
Rivers (freshwater)	1,200	0.0001
Total	1,270,000,000	100

Worldwide, water is becoming a critical resource. Statistically, 71% of the Earth is covered by water. However, approximately 97% of this water is salt water. Only 3% is freshwater, and of that, about 2.997% is unavailable as it is locked away in polar ice or deep aquifers. **Only about 0.003%** of the water on Earth is actually available for human activities.

CAPT Review Questions 5-6

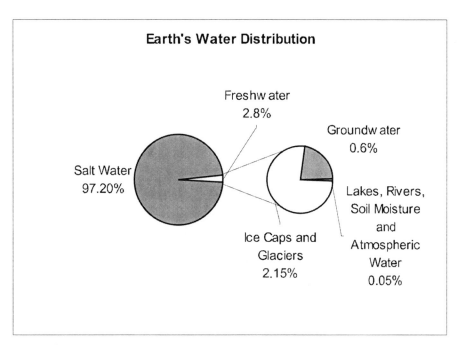

Figure 9-4. Accompanies Review Questions 5-6

5. The graph above shows the distribution of the Earth's water resources. According to the graph most of Earth's freshwater is in the
   a. lakes, rivers, soil, and atmosphere
   b. ground
   c. icecaps and glaciers
   d. ocean

6. If the people of the world polluted the groundwater supply, the percentage of Earth's freshwater (excluding the water frozen at the poles) left for human consumption would be
   a. 3.0%
   b. 2.14%
   c. 0.05%
   d. 0.015%

Answers to CAPT Review Questions 5-6

5. **The correct answer is c.** The icecaps and the glaciers make up 2.14% of the Earth's water, which is the highest of the freshwater categories. Lakes, rivers, soil, and atmosphere only contain only 0.015% of the Earth's water. Groundwater only makes up 0.61% of the Earth's water. While ocean water makes up almost 97.24% of the Earth's water, it is not freshwater.

6. **The correct answer is d.** If the water at the icecaps is excluded and the groundwater is polluted, then the only water left is the water in lakes, rivers, the soil, and the atmosphere, which totals 0.015%. The total amount of freshwater available is 3%; however, the question excluded water from the icecaps, glaciers, and groundwater. The total amount of water frozen at the icecap is 2.14%. The amount of groundwater that is polluted and, therefore, not drinkable is 0.61%.

How Can We Run Out of Water If It Is a Renewable Resource?

The average American uses about 95 m^3 of water a year. In arid and semiarid regions, water may become a nonrenewable resource as people demand more water for irrigation and industrial use than falls or passes through their area in the course of a year. In parts of southwestern United States, much of the water that has been pumped out of the ground for agricultural and residential use comes from a nonrenewable ice age aquifer.

How Are Freshwater Supplies Managed?

The supply of freshwater can be managed using reservoirs to store surplus water, aqueducts to move it to areas with less water, deep wells to remove groundwater, and water treatment facilities to clean polluted water. Desalination of sea water may be used in some areas with scarce freshwater.

The near future may see major changes in how we manage one of our most important natural resources, water. However, it is beginning to look like there is not enough water to do everything we would like to do. It may be an abundant resource here in Connecticut, but it is not an unlimited resource.

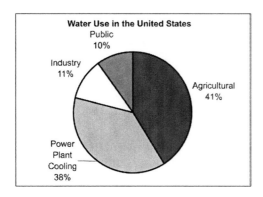
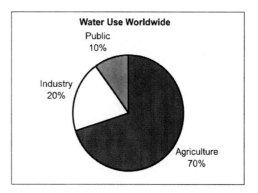

Figures 9-5. A and B: Accompanies Review Questions 7-8

CAPT Review Questions 7-8

7. Based on graphs A and B above, both Americans and people worldwide use most of their freshwater for
   a. public utilities (water used by homes and businesses)
   b. industrial purposes
   c. power plant cooling
   d. agriculture

8. If the United Nations wanted to develop a plan to conserve water worldwide, the best plan would involve
   a. lawn-watering restrictions for homeowners
   b. low flow showerheads for homes
   c. better irrigation systems for farms
   d. mandated water recycling for industry

Answers to Review Questions 7-8

7. **The correct answer is d.** A total of 41% of the water in the United States and 70% of the water worldwide is used for agriculture, which is the largest category on graphs A and B. Only 10% of the water is used for public utilities in both the United States and around the world. Only 11% of the water is used for industry in

the United States, and only 20% of the water is used by industry worldwide. Power plant cooling only represents 38% of the water used in the United States and is not even on the world usage graph.

8. **The correct answer is c.** Water for agriculture represents the largest strain on our freshwater resources, so developing irrigation that would use less water has the potential to save the most water. Public utilities represent only 10% of the total water usage, so conservation would not have the biggest impact. Industry uses only 20% of the water supply, so industry-use reforms would not have as drastic an impact as reforms in agricultural practice.

Energy

After reviewing this section, you should be able to answer the following questions:
What is the Earth's most important source of energy?
What is geothermal energy?
How do we categorize our energy resources?
How is electricity generated from fossil fuels and uranium?
How are the fossil fuels formed?
What are some drawbacks to using fossil fuels?
What is the source of nuclear power?
What are the major drawbacks of nuclear power?
How is geothermal power produced?
What are the pros and cons of wind power?
What are the advantages and disadvantages of hydroelectric power?
What is the difference between active and passive solar power?
What is the difference between biomass, biogas, alcohol, and trash as energy sources?
Why hasn't tidal and wave power become major energy resources?
What are some nonrenewable energy resources that could be major sources of fuel?

What Is the Earth's Most Important Source of Energy?

The sun has always been the major source of energy for the Earth's surface. Its winds and ocean currents are the result of the sun's uneven heating of the surface. The sun's light provides the energy to power photosynthesis in plants, which is the basis of the Earth's food chain. Without the sun, the Earth would freeze solid to a depth of hundreds of meters.

What Is Geothermal Energy?

Below a depth of several hundred meters, the sun's heat is not felt; it is the heat from the Earth's interior, geothermal energy, that keeps it warm. The Earth's mantle's temperature ranges from 6000°C near the core to 2000°C at the base of the crust. Near plate boundaries and hot spots, the heat may be concentrated, melting rock, forming magma. The rising magma may heat up the nearby crustal rocks along with any water or gas that they may contain to temperatures well above boiling.

How Do We Categorize Our Energy Resources?

Most of the energy resources we use today are tied to solar energy. Like our other natural resources, they are divided into nonrenewable and renewable categories. Nonrenewable energy resources are those of which there are limited amounts. Renewable energy resources are those that can be replenished as they are used.

How Is Electricity Generated from Fossil Fuels and Uranium?

The major nonrenewable energy resources are fossil fuels and uranium. Power is generated when the heat from burning fossil fuels or radioactive decay is used to boil water. The steam from the boiling water is used to spin turbines, which turn generators that actually generate the electricity we use.

How Are the Fossil Fuels Formed?

Fossil fuels—natural gas (CH_4), peat, coal, and petroleum—are formed from the remains of organisms that lived millions of years ago. Petroleum was formed from the oil found within the bodies of marine phytoplankton. Heat and pressure in the crust began to cook the sediment containing the remains, slowly driving out the oil and water. The oil and water forced out of the rock slowly worked their way up through pores in the rock. If they encounter a layer of nonporous rock they become trapped, forming an oil reservoir.

Peat and coal are formed from the partially decayed remains of plants. Most coal formed in great swamps, which once covered the interiors of what was North America and Eurasia. The plants died and fell into the swamp's stagnant water, where they were preserved. As the land slowly sank, additional deposits began to compress the plant material. As the temperatures and pressures increased, the water and gasses were driven out of the remains, creating bituminous or soft coal. If additional heat and pressure were added, such as when two continents collided, almost all the gas and water were driven out, creating anthracite or hard coal.

Natural gas or methane may be formed by the decomposition of organic material. Bacteria decomposing plant material also generate natural gas. As coal or oil is being heated and compressed, natural gas may be given off as a by-product. Some methane may actually be left over from the formation of Earth.

What Are Some Drawbacks to Using Fossil Fuels?

Our reliance on fossil fuels has created numerous problems. The burning of fossil fuels releases carbon dioxide, nitrogen, and sulfur into the atmosphere and thus contributes to air pollution and the greenhouse effect. Hot water from the power plant affects life in nearby rivers, lakes, or oceans. The sulfur and nitrogen released by the burning fuel combines with water to create acid rain. The underground mining of coal is an extremely hazardous occupation due to cave-ins, explosions, and fires. The strip mining of coal near the surface may disrupt thousands of acres with digging and the piling up of waste rock and dirt. Runoff from mining and drilling sites may result in water pollution. Oil spills from ruptured pipelines or sinking tanker ships may pollute the land and ocean and harm wildlife. Today, fossil fuels do provide the bulk of our energy production and transportation needs. However, we have already used up the cheap, easily extracted oil and coal. At the rate of usage today, most scientists believe that accessible supplies will be depleted within several hundred years, and unfortunately, demand is growing.

CAPT Review Questions 9-10

Arianna took a commuter bus to visit the city. On the side of the bus was a sign that said the bus was powered by natural gas to help the environment. Arianna was interested in the environment and wanted to know about natural gas and its uses. She found the graph below.

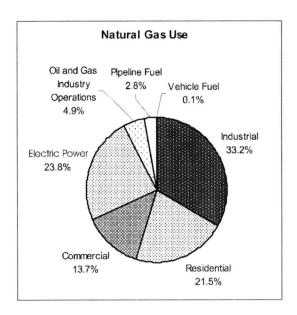

Figure 9-6. Accompanies Review Questions 9-10

9. Based on the graph above, what portion of the natural gas in the United States is used power vehicles like the bus Arianna took to the city?
   a. 23.8%
   b. 13.7%
   c. 4.9%
   d. 0.1%

10. The sign on the bus said that using natural gas was helping the environment. Natural gas is considered better for the environment then oil, gasoline, or coal because
    a. it makes natural gas vehicles lighter then gasoline vehicles
    b. we can burn natural gas easier then coal, gasoline, or oil
    c. natural gas is more abundant than coal, gasoline, or oil
    d. natural gas has fewer impurities then coal, gasoline, and oil so it produces less pollution

Answers to CAPT Review Questions 9-10

9. **The correct answer is d.** A total of 0.1% is the amount of natural gas used to power vehicles, but 23.8% is the amount of natural gas used to generate electric power. A total of 13.7% is the amount of natural gas used by the commercial sector, and 4.9 % is the amount of natural gas used by the oil and gas industry.

10. **The correct answer is d.** Natural gas has fewer impurities than coal, oil, and gasoline, so when it is burned, it produces less sulfur dioxide and nitrogen oxides, which is better for the environment. The weight of natural gas has no effect on the environment. The ease with which we can burn natural gas, coal, gasoline, or oil is not related to how harmful it is to the environment. The abundance of natural gas is not related to its impact on the environment when it is burned.

What Is the Source of Nuclear Power?

Nuclear power is a possible alternative to fossil fuels for generating electricity. A significant portion, if not all our electrical needs could be met by using nuclear power. A nuclear reactor harnesses the heat energy released by the fission of uranium-235 (U-235) atoms. Uranium is rare, and U-235 is a rare isotope of uranium. When enough U-235 is placed within the fuel rods of a nuclear reactor, along with the nonradioactive isotope uranium-238 (U-238), the radioactive breakdown of the atoms results in a chain reaction between the atoms in the fuel rod, which generates enough heat to boil water.

What Are the Major Drawbacks of Nuclear Power?

When a nuclear reactor is working properly, there is no air pollution. Most of the problems associated with nuclear power surround the waste products. In nuclear reactors, the nonradioactive U-238 may become the radioactive element plutonium, an effective fuel for atomic bombs. All material that comes into contact with the core of the reactor will become radioactive. The material that comes into contact with the radioactive material may also become radioactive. The particle radiation given off by radioactive material may destroy plant and animal cells, or it may cause harmful changes to the genetic material within cells. The wastes remain radioactive for tens of thousands of years. How and where to store the wastes are major problems. In the past, a great deal of waste was sealed in barrels and dumped into the ocean or stored on site at the nuclear reactors. However, the barrels may slowly break down in the ocean, leaking waste into the sea. Communities with nuclear reactors worry about the dangers of having wastes stored in their town. In the future, much of the United States' radioactive waste will be stored in underground salt mines or mines dug into stable rock layers of the Earth, where hopefully the waste will be stored for thousands of years without being disturbed.

How Is Geothermal Power Produced?

In some areas, geothermal energy is being used to produce energy. In areas of the western United States, magma has been near enough to the surface to heat the rock within the crust to well above boiling. To generate power, wells have to be dug into the hot rock, then cold water is pumped into the ground. The water going down is boiled by the rock. The return pipes lead the steam to turbines, which turn generators. The major problems associated with geothermal energy is that its usefulness is limited to relatively few areas on the Earth's surface where magma is near the surface and there are nearby population centers. In addition, the constant flow of cool water down the wells slowly cools off the rock, slowly eliminating the source of the power.

Renewable energy resources are constantly being renewed as we use them. In today's energy-dependent society, there is such a demand for electricity and oil that we are starting to experience shortages. Unless we find new sources of energy or new ways to use old renewable sources, then we may find that our high-tech society does not have enough power to keep running.

What Are the Pros and Cons of Wind Power?

Wind power is gaining popularity in areas with strong, consistent winds, such coastlines, ridges, and plains. Wind farms, with hundreds of giant propeller driven wind turbines can produce enough power to run a small town. It is not possible to rely on wind power because no matter where the location, the wind does not always blow. In addition, people may object to the sight of hundreds of wind turbines along ridges and off the coast. Even out on the continental shelf, out of sight of most people, there is concern for marine navigation and migratory sea birds flying north or south along the coast.

CAPT Review Questions 11-12

Wind power is becoming a more popular alternative energy source. Below is a chart that shows the states that generate some of their power using wind.

State	Megawatts of Power Being Generated by Wind
Alaska	0.8
California	1,713
Colorado	62.2
Hawaii	1.6
Iowa	324.2
Kansas	113.7
Maine	1
Massachusetts	1
Michigan	2.4
Minnesota	319.1
Nebraska	2.8
New Mexico	1.3
New York	48.2
Oregon	157.5
Pennsylvania	34.5
South Dakota	2.6
Tennessee	2
Texas	1,095.5
Vermont	6
Washington	178.2
Wisconsin	53

11. The most wind power is generated on the
    a. East Coast
    b. Midwest
    c. West Coast
    d. Alaska and Hawaii

12. Wind power is a more attractive alternative to burning fossil fuel because
    a. it generates less noise
    b. it produces less radioactive waste
    c. we have already adapted large sections of the country to use it
    d. it is naturally abundant and produces less pollution

Answers to CAPT Review Questions 11-12

11. **The correct answer is c.** The West Coast states (California, Oregon, Washington) generate over 2000 megawatts of power from wind energy. The states along the East Coast generate less the 100 megawatts of power from wind energy. The midwestern states, even if you include Texas, still generate less than 2000 megawatts of power from wind energy. Alaska and Hawaii combined only generate 2.4 megawatts of power from wind energy.

12. **The correct answer is d.** Wind is an almost limitless resource, and wind turbines generate very little pollution. Wind turbines actually produce more noise then power plants that burn fossil fuel. Wind power does not produce radioactive waste. Less then half the states in the United States produce wind energy.

What Are the Advantages and Disadvantages of Hydroelectric Power?

Flowing water once powered grain and lumber mills in towns all over Connecticut. Water running through a hydroelectric dam uses spin turbines, which are used to turn generators. Hydroquebec, which has dammed many rivers in Quebec, is an important contributor to Connecticut's power grid. Connecticut has some relatively small hydroelectric dams on the Farmington and Housatonic Rivers.

Hydroelectricity does provide a consistent, nonpolluting source of power. The reservoirs behind the dam often become recreational areas for boating and water skiing. However, the river damming alters the flow pattern of the stream below the dam. Water behind the dam tends to heat up in the summer as compared to a free-flowing river, which affects the type of fish that can live there. The dam also traps sediment moving down the river. Sediment then is no longer available to enrich floodplain farmland, the marshes at the mouth of the river, or replace sediment lost to coast erosion.

What Is the Difference between Active and Passive Solar Power?

Solar power is among the most promising of renewable alternative energy resources. Solar energy may be collected passively or actively. Passive solar systems use sunlight directly to provide light or heat. A typical window is an example of a passive solar system. Windows allow light and heat to enter a room. Active solar systems use solar cells or photovoltaic cells to convert light into electricity. Solar panels use sunlight to heat water. Active systems are still generally expensive and are used only on a small scale. Even if the cost of solar cells comes way down, such an extensive amount of land would have to be covered with cells to provide electricity for a town; thus, in Connecticut, it would not be economical to do so as land is very expensive. There is also problem of what do you do
after the sun goes down or on the short days of winter when energy is most needed.

What Is the Difference between Biomass, Biogas, Alcohol, and Trash as Energy Sources?

Biomass, material derived from living things, is an alternative renewable resource. In the past, whale oil, dried dung, and reeds were used as fuel. Much of the world still relies on wood as a source of fuel. The problems associated with wood burning are the same as burning fossil fuels. Home stoves and fire places are not nearly as efficient as power plants and may become major local sources of pollution.

Biogas is a mixture of methane and carbon dioxide. Organic material, including manure, is dumped into a large container called a digester where bacteria break down the waste. Once the waste is broken down, it is removed from the digester, dried, and then used as fertilizer. In the past, this was associated with farms; today many municipalities use it in conjunction with their sewer treatment plants. Some cities use gas generated by their sewer plants to power the plant and run municipal vehicles. There may be certain health hazards, such as bacterial and viral contamination, associated with using municipal waste for fertilizers.

Alcohol is a cleaner burning renewable alternative to petroleum. Alcohol is derived from the fermentation of organic material. Corn may be grown, and the corn kernels used to produce ethanol, an alcohol that may be added to gasoline. Gasohol, the combination of gasoline and alcohol, burns well in most automobile engines. The corn plant could be used as fuel to burn in a power plant.

Trash may also be used to fuel energy plants. A community's trash, minus recyclables, consists largely of paper and other organic products that can be burned as a fuel. This does allow a town a way to get rid of much of its trash, without filling up landfills, but the trash ash could be contaminated with any number of pollutants, including metals such as mercury.

Why Hasn't Tidal and Wave Power Become Major Energy Resources?

The ocean is a source of several other potential alternative energy resources. Where tides are high, enough dam-like structures may be placed across bays and the water moving into or out of the bay could turn turbines in the dam. There are relatively few places in the United States, such as some inlets in Maine or Alaska where the tide would be high enough for effective tidal power plants. The negative aspects of tidal power include the disruption of coastal marine life and the potential high maintenance costs to keep the plants running. Salt water is very corrosive, and marine life such as barnacles and muscles could foul the machinery and pipes. Wave action may also produce some electricity. The up and down action of waves could be used to drive a piston up and down in a buoy, which could generate electricity. Like wind power, wave power is very unreliable, and it may disrupt marine life or become a navigation hazard.

What Are Some Nonrenewable Energy Resources That Could Be Major Sources of Fuel?

In addition to renewable alternative energy resources, there are nonrenewable alternative energy resources that could impact our energy supply. Oil shale and tar sand contain a raw form of hydrocarbon, which may be processed to produce oil or gas. Tar sands form where crude oil seeps to the surface without being trapped. Oil shale is the type of rock, which, if it was deeply buried and under great heat and pressure, would release its trapped hydrocarbons. This can be done artificially by crushing the mined rock and then heating it until the hydrocarbons in it vaporize; the resulting gas can be condensed and refined into oil and gasoline. Vast deposits of oil shale found in the western United States have the potential to equal the energy equivalent of the entire world's petroleum supply.

At this time, it is still much more expensive to mine and refine oil shale than it is to buy even the most expensive overseas oil. The mining requires a great deal of water, which is already in short supply in the West. Additionally, because of the grinding process needed to extract the oil, there is a greater volume of waste product than there was of original rock. If you were to dig a pit mine on the plains to remove oil shale, when you were done mining and pushed all the waste back into the pit, you would be left with a hill.

Curriculum Embedded Performance Task

Strand I: Energy Transformations Laboratory
Solar Cooker

In this laboratory investigation, you designed an experiment to assess the effectiveness of one possible renewable source of energy for one purpose: the use of solar energy in the cooking/heating of food. Given the basic design of a solar cooker, you were asked to test the effect of one variable on the performance of your cooker in terms of its ability to increase the temperature of water. You could test shape, position, color, or material of your cooker. As you review this experiment, remember to consider each of the following questions:

What is the independent variable? The dependent variable?

What type of graph would be appropriate for graphing the data obtained in this lab?

1. What can the shape of your graph tell you about the underlying variables being measured?
2. What features of this experiment were you able to control?
3. How were you able to control these features?
4. What features of this experiment were not able to be controlled? Why?
5. How confident are you in the results of this experiment?
6. How valid is this experiment? Remember to consider how well the designed experiment measures the stated problem, the ability to control the experiment, the amount of data collected, and the reliability of the collected data.

Curriculum Embedded Performance Task

Strand I: Energy Transformations Science, Technology, and Society
Energy Uses in Connecticut

In this embedded task, you were given information about the trends in Connecticut Energy Use over the past several years, including numerical data about the amounts of different types of energy utilized throughout the state. After selecting and assembling an appropriate graph of this information, you examined the pros and cons of one energy trend that you selected. Some possible trends you may have examined include: the increase in the use of water energy in the state, the increase in the use of fossil fuel energy, the increase in the use of nuclear energy, and the decrease in the use of coal energy.

As you consider each energy source, remember to consider not only the direct impact on the lives of humans, but also the effects on the environment, ecosystems, and other living organisms.

Chapter 10:
Matter Cycling
and Climate Change

Water Cycle

After reviewing this section, you should be able to answer the following questions:

From where did the Earth's water come?

What is the water cycle?

Where is the Earth's water stored?

How does water enter the atmosphere?

How do clouds form?

How does precipitation form?

Where does the water go once it hits the ground?

What is acid rain? Why is Acid rain a problem?

From Where Did the Earth's Water Come?

In over 4 billion years, the Earth's supply of water has barely changed. Most of our water came with the original ices that formed the Earth. Some water has been lost as water molecules that have been broken apart by sunlight in the upper atmosphere, and some new water has been added through volcanic eruptions and comet impacts. However, the Earth has been recycling its water since the first rains fell.

What Is the Water Cycle?

The water cycle is the continuous process by which water moves from the atmosphere to the surface of the Earth and then back again. It involves the evaporation of stored water, condensation, precipitation, and runoff, which leads back to water storage and evaporation.

Where Is the Earth's Water Stored?

The World's Water

Location	Water Volume (km³)	Percentage of Total Water	Estimated Time in Storage
Oceans (saltwater)	1,230,000,000	97.24	Thousands of years
Glaciers (freshwater)	28,600,000	2.14	UP to hundreds of thousands of years
Groundwater (freshwater)	8,000,000	0.615	Months to hundreds of thousands of years
Lakes (freshwater)	123,000	0.009	Tens of years
Atmosphere (freshwater)	12,700	0.001	9 days
Rivers (freshwater)	1200	0.0001	Days to weeks
Total	1,270,000,000	100	4+ billion years

The bulk of Earth's freshwater is stored in the continental glaciers of Antarctica Greenland. Most groundwater is found within the pore spaces within the soil and sedimentary rock. In an aquifer, as much as 40% of the volume of the soil or rock may be water. Below about 10 km, the pressure crushes the pores together. Below that there is still a great deal of water, but it is chemically bound to minerals within the crust and may be released during volcanic eruptions.

How Does Water Enter the Atmosphere?

The sun's energy drives the water cycle by providing the energy for the **evaporation** of the water. Water may evaporate from any moist or liquid surface; plant leaves, damp soil, freshwater lakes, the ocean, or even falling rain. Every day about 1,200 km³ of water evaporate. **Transpiration** is an important source of atmospheric water in tropical rain forests. Ice may turn into a gas through the process of **sublimation**. The rates of evaporation and sublimation increase with temperature, the intensity of the sunlight, and wind speed. It slows as the humidity increases. Evaporation rates can range from nearly zero on the polar ice caps to as much as 4 m of water a year over tropical forests and warm ocean currents; the average worldwide is about 1 m/yr.

How Do Clouds Form?

When warm air rises, the air expands, and it undergoes what is called **adiabatic cooling**. Clouds form when the rising air cools below the **dew point**, the temperature at which air must be cooled to become saturated. Clouds may also form when air is forced up the side of a mountain where it may reach the dew point. Clouds may also form when a mass of warm moist air meets cool air; the cool air absorbs the heat energy of the warm air. Clouds and perhaps precipitation may form in the cooling air mass along the front formed by the colliding air masses.

How Does Precipitation Form?

Every day approximately 1,200 km³ of water fall to the Earth as precipitation. The four main types of **precipitation** are rain, snow, sleet, and hail. They all initially form in clouds where water vapor condenses as ice or water on particles of dust or salt (**condensation nuclei**) in the atmosphere. Precipitation occurs when the snow flakes or water droplets become too heavy to be held up in the cloud by the air currents. Sleet starts as rain but freezes as it drops from a warm air mass through cold air near the ground. Hail forms when powerful updrafts in thunderclouds carry droplets high enough so that they freeze. When the hail drops back down in the clouds, it picks up an additional layer of water before the updrafts in the clouds carry the hail back up. Eventually, the hail is too large to be carried by the wind, and it falls to the ground. Precipitation can be extremely heavy. A typical thunderstorm can drop 0.1 km³ on a small area of land in just a few hours. A major storm may drop 100 km³ of precipitation over a period of several days.

Where Does the Water Go Once It Hits the Ground?

Rivers carry about 20% of the rain to the ocean. Most rainwater soaks into the soil and works its way through the pores in the dirt or bedrock to become groundwater. Water that seeps through the ground moves slowly, usually less than a meter a day. However, because so much of the precipitation is absorbed by the ground, it represents our largest reservoir of usable freshwater. Plant roots absorb water from the dirt, and through capillary action, it is carried up through the plant to its leaves. The leaves give off excess water in the process of transpiration. Water that soaks through the ground may fill depressions in the ground, creating ponds or lakes. Where water moving through the ground intersects the surface, springs may form.

Eventually rainwater reaches the sea or evaporates, and the cycle renews itself. However, there is only a limited amount of available freshwater, and the supply can change with the weather or long-term climatic change.

What is acid rain?

Acids are any substances with a pH of less than 7. In an unpolluted atmosphere, precipitation falls from the sky and mixes largely with carbon dioxide gas. In this situation, the pH of that rain water, snow, or other form of precipitation would be close to 6, because the carbon dioxide in combination with water forms a weak acid. However, the burning of fossil fuels in automobiles, factories, and industry leads to the production of several unintended by-products, including sulfur dioxide and nitrogen oxides. These compounds, when dissolved in water, can have a pH that is much lower (3-4 range).

Why is acid rain a problem?

Many of the building materials used by humans react with acids. Acids can wear away quickly at buildings, various types of rock, and other materials. Further, the acid in acid rain can mix with soil in the ground and in lakes, streams, and oceans, eventually altering the pH of these areas, affecting the balance of ecosystems.

Curriculum Embedded Performance Task

Strand III: Global Interdependence Science, Technology, and Society
Connecticut Brownfield Sites

Brownfield sites are parts of the human environment, previously used as sites of industry, that have been contaminated in some way. Often, these sites are deserted, unusable, and pose potential health risks for humans (and animals) in the area. The specific effects of some of the contaminants are not well studied and are therefore unknown. In this task, you were asked to design (but not carry out) a controlled experiment to study the effects of Brownfield contamination on one part of the local environment. To design an informative experiment, you must remember to keep your problem narrow; do not try to focus on too many things at once. As you consider your experimental design, remember to consider the following questions:

1. What is the independent variable? The dependent variable?
2. What type of graph would be appropriate for graphing the data obtained in this lab?
3. What can the shape of your graph tell you about the underlying variables being measured?
4. What features of this experiment are you able to control?
5. How are you able to control these features?
6. What features of this experiment are not able to be controlled? Why?
7. What results would you expect from this experiment, and what will these results tell you about your problem?
8. How valid is this experiment? Remember to consider how well the designed experiment measures the stated problem, the ability to control the experiment, the amount of data collected, and the reliability of the collected data.

CAPT Review Questions 1-2

Ranjit brought a cold glass of water outside on a humid day. After being outside for only a minute or two, the glass was covered with water. Ranjit wanted to find out from where the water on the outside of the glass came, so he looked up information and found the diagram below.

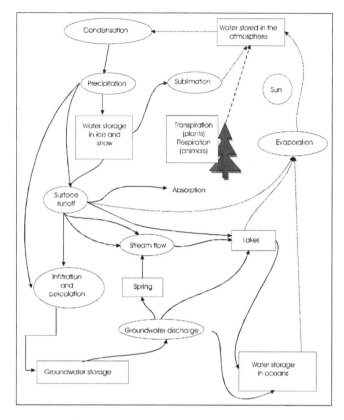

Figure 10-1. Accompanies Review Questions 1-2

1. The water on Ranjit's glass most likely
   a. sublimated from the ice in the water
   b. seeped through the glass from the inside
   c. condensed from the atmosphere
   d. stayed on the glass after Ranjit's sweaty hand put it down

2. Based on the figure above, once Ranjit drinks the glass of water, it will most likely re-enter the water cycle when Ranjit
   a. sleeps
   b. breathes
   c. eats
   d. exercises

Answers to CAPT Review Questions 1-2

1. **The correct answer is c.** The cold glass causes the water vapor in the atmosphere to condense when it comes in contact with it, similar to steam condensing on the windows of a house or a car when it is cold outside. Water that sublimated from the ice in the glass would be in the form of water vapor, which is a gas, not a liquid. The glass is not permeable to water or, in other words, does not let water pass

through it. If it were, it would always be leaking water. Most likely, Ranjit's hands did produce enough sweat to cover the outside of the glass. However, additional observation would show that the amount of water on the outside of the glass continued to increase long after the glass was put down, so the water could not be coming from Ranjit's hands.

2. **The correct answer is b.** Based on the diagram of the water cycle, animals return water to the atmosphere when they breathe not when they sleep, eat, or exercise.

Curriculum Embedded Performance Task

Strand III: Global Interdependence Laboratory
Acid Rain

In this laboratory, you designed an experiment to test resistance of various building materials to acid. As you consider this experiment, you should remember that some materials react quickly with acid, while other may wear down over longer periods of time. Remember that basic materials (like limestone) will tend to react more quickly. Remember also to consider the following questions as you think about any experiment:

1. What is the independent variable? The dependent variable?
2. What type of graph would be appropriate for graphing the data obtained in this lab?
3. What can the shape of your graph tell you about the underlying variables being measured?
4. What features of this experiment were you able to control?
5. How were you able to control these features?
6. What features of this experiment were not able to be controlled? Why?
7. How confident are you in the results of this experiment?
8. How valid is this experiment? Remember to consider how well the designed experiment measures the stated problem, the ability to control the experiment, the amount of data collected, and the reliability of the collected data.

Climate

After reviewing this section, you should be able to answer the following questions:

What is the difference between climatology and meteorology?

How are Earth's climates categorized?

Why can Connecticut be as hot as the tropics in summer and as cold as the poles in winter?

How do the Earth's wind patterns affect climate?

How does the distribution of land and ocean affect the climate?

How does topography affect an area's climate?

What Is the Difference between Climatology and Meteorology?

Meteorology is the study of the weather. **Climatology** is the study of **climates**, the average, long-term weather conditions for an area. One of Earth's unique features is its wide range of climates. From frigid polar deserts to hot tropical rainforest, no other known planet has such a diverse range of surface environments.

How Are Earth's Climates Categorized?

Climate categories are based on the annual and monthly averages of temperature and precipitation. Climatologists generally recognize six major types of climate, which are subdivided into eleven **subclimates**.

The Earth's Climates

Climate	Subclimate	Description
Polar	Tundra	A short cool, dry summer, below freezing most of year
	Icecap	Perennial ice, temperature below freezing all year
Dry	Desert	Evaporation > precipitation throughout the year
	Semiarid	Evaporation > precipitation during most of the year
Humid tropical	Tropical wet	Precipitation and average temperatures above 18°C (72°F) all year
	Tropical wet and dry	Above 18°C all year but with pronounced wet and dry seasons
Moist mid-latitude With mild winters	Humid subtropical	Hot summer and mild winters with precipitation all year
	Marine West Coast	Mild and rainy all year
	Mediterranean	Hot and dry summers; mild and rainy winters
Moist mid-latitude with severe winters	Humid continental	Warm rainy summers and cold snowy winters
	Subarctic	Short cool summers and long cold snowy winters
Highland	No subclimates	Climate affected by altitude; wide variation in temperature and precipitation

The climate of a particular region is controlled by a number of variables. These include: the intensity of the solar radiation, global wind patterns, formation of air masses, and the topography of the land.

Why Is Connecticut as Hot as the Tropics in the Summer and as Cold as the Poles in the Winter?

The most important aspect of climate is the amount of solar radiation an area receives. At the equator, the sun's light is consistently intense. Every day it is out for nearly 12 hours and passes nearly overhead at noon. As you move north or south, the length of sunlight increases as you move from the winter solstice to the summer solstice (and the reverse for the second half of the year). Above the Arctic Circle, there are 24 hours of sunlight on the first day of summer. However, the sunlight hitting the surface is at such a low angle that it tends to reflect off the surface rather than be absorbed. Therefore, temperatures at the poles seldom rise to 32°F, above which ice would melt. In Connecticut, on the first day of summer, the sun is out for nearly 14 hours and travels a path nearly as high in the sky as it does in the tropics. This results in tropical-like conditions. In the winter the sun is out for only about 9 hours and is as low as the sun's arctic summer path. This results in polar type conditions

How Do the Earth's Wind Patterns Affect Climate?

The Earth's wind patterns are driven by a combination of the effects of solar radiation at different latitudes and the rotation of the Earth. Following the equator, in the belt of equatorial lows, air rises and cools, and water condenses, falling as rain. As a result, surrounding the Earth is a warm belt with high rainfall. As you move north or south to the area around latitudes 20° and 30°, you enter the subtropical highs, where air is sinking and heating up. These are the locations of the world's great deserts. As you move into the **temperate zones**, as in most of the United States, precipitation increases because of the constant interaction of polar air moving south and tropical air moving north. Remember that climate is the long-term average of the weather for a location. Unlike the tropics or the poles, temperate areas may receive wide variations in the actual amount of rain and snow they receive in a given year. Above 60° latitude the amount of precipitation decreases due to the polar high pressure. As the seasons, change so due these belts. On the summer solstice, the sun is most intense over the Tropic of Cancer; this shifts the equatorial lows north. On the winter solstice, the sun is most intense over the Tropic of Capricorn; this may result in land areas moving from one wind belt into another. An area at the northern edge of the equatorial low may shift into the subtropical highs and its dry weather in the winter and back into the rain for the summer. The weather pattern may be controlled by the trade winds in one season and the westerlies in another.

How Does the Distribution of Land and Ocean Affect the Climate?

The Earth's climates also influence the distribution of land and water, ocean currents, and mountains. A land mass absorbs and releases heat much faster than a body of water. The air over a continent heats up more in the summer than surrounding oceans, creating a large low-pressure region. If there is no available water source, the air might be very hot and dry. In the winter, the same land mass cools off much faster than the water, creating a high-pressure system. Ocean currents carry warm water from the tropics toward the poles. Air blowing over the water becomes warm and humid from evaporating sea water. As it moves across the land, it warms the land, and as it cools, it creates fog, mist, or rain. Water temperature affects the rate of evaporation. The air downwind of a warm current has more moisture than air downwind of a cold current.

The air over a land mass or body of water may take on characteristics associated with the source region.

Air Mass Type	Source	Characteristics
A	Arctic	Bitter cold, dry
cP	Continental polar	Very cold, dry
cT	Continental tropical	Warm, dry
mP	Marine polar	Cold, humid
mT	Marine tropical	Warm, humid

Once an air mass moves out of its place of origin, it carries the regions characteristics with it. In Connecticut's climate, we experience both bone-chilling arctic blasts and oppressively humid tropical heat waves.

How Does Topography Affect an Area's Climate?

Topography can also influence climate, particularly the presence of mountain ranges. If the prevailing winds are forced up a mountain range, the air cools and loses most of its moisture through precipitation. On the West Coast of the United States, the Cascade Mountains have rain forests on their western side where the winds are forced up the slopes. However, this means that the air flowing back down the other side has been drained of moisture. As the air moves back down slope, it heats up due to compression. Often there is what is referred to as a rain shadow on the downwind side of a mountain range.

Mountains may have planet-wide climatic consequences. There may be a link between the Himalayas, the world's tallest mountains, and the ice age. Prior to India colliding with Asia, that area of the world was subtropical ocean. Solar energy striking there was absorbed and distributed by ocean currents northward. The modern Himalayas are so high that their peaks are snow covered. Now they reflect the sunlight that used to be absorbed by the ocean. Some scientists believe that is what started the Earth's cooling trend, which hopefully climaxed in the last great glacial advance, which began its retreat only 18,000 years ago.

CAPT Review Questions 3-4

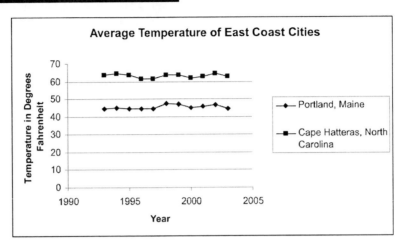

Figure 10-2. Accompanies Review Questions 7-8

3. Portland, Maine, and Cape Hatteras, North Carolina, are both located on the East Coast of the United States. Based on the figure above, it is reasonable to conclude that
   a. Cape Hatteras has a wetter climate than Portland.
   b. When Cape Hatteras is warm, Portland is cold.
   c. Cape Hatteras has a warmer climate than Portland.
   d. Both Cape Hatteras and Portland have been experiencing a drop in average temperature over the last 35 years.

4. The differences between Portland, Maine, and Cape Hatteras, North Carolina, are caused by differences in the
   a. amount of rainfall each location receives.
   b. amount of sunlight each location receives.
   c. elevation of each location.
   d. amount of cloud cover at each location.

Answers to CAPT Review Questions 3-4

3. **The correct answer is c.** Cape Hatteras is generally warmer than Portland. The figure contains no information about precipitation. The figure does not show a consistent pattern of increase in temperature at Cape Hatteras when there is a decrease in Portland. Both Cape Hatteras and Portland have been experiencing a steady rise in temperature over the last 35 years.

4. **The correct answer is b.** The difference in temperature between Cape Hatteras, North Carolina, and Portland, Maine, is caused by the difference in their latitude. Cape Hatteras's more southern location means it gets more direct sunlight than

Portland, making it warmer. There is no information in the figure concerning the amount of rainfall each city receives. Both cities are coastal cities, which means they have approximately the same elevation. There is no information to indicate a difference in cloud cover over each of the cities.

Global Weather Phenomena

After reviewing this section,, you should be able to answer the following questions:

What are El Niño and La Niña?

What is the ozone hole?

How are global warming and the greenhouse effect defined?

How can changes in Earth's albedo influence the changes in climate?

What might be the effects of global warming?

Introduction

Everybody knows the weather changes. However, within anyone's lifetime, the climate seems stable, but it is also subject to cycles and long-term change. Within the long-term climate, there are short-term changes that may be the result of natural cycles within the hydrosphere and atmosphere, such as El Niño and La Niña. There are other changes to the atmosphere that man certainly has a hand in creating. The depletion of ozone in the atmosphere can be strongly tied to the production of manmade chemicals, **chlorofluorocarbons (CFCs)**. Major long-term climate changes are occurring as a result of CFCs. Only 15,000 years ago much of the North America and Europe was in the grip of a major ice age. We are now in the longest, warmest interglacial period in 120,000 years. Earth appears to be getting warmer, and man's activities may play a part.

What Are El Niño and La Niña?

The term **El Niño** means "Christ Child" and was first used by South American fisherman to describe the warm ocean currents that sometimes appeared off the coast of Peru in December. **La Niña** is the opposite condition, when unusually cold water appears. They appear to be part of an oscillation of conditions across the Pacific Ocean.

Normally atmospheric and ocean currents transport cold water from the Antarctic up along the west coast of South America and westward across the ocean. The trade winds and equatorial currents keep warm water in the western Pacific. A warm pressure area located over the warm western Pacific creates cloudiness and heavy precipitation over Southeast Asia and northern Australia. However, every 3-5 years the trade winds die down, and the surface currents carrying the cool water along the Equator stop flowing. As a result, the warm western Pacific waters surge eastward across the ocean. This significantly warms the waters off the west coast of South America. This change in surface temperatures of the ocean sets off changes in the normal weather around the world. The normally cool dry conditions along much of the coast of South America become warmer and much more humid. Increased evaporation and strong convection raise the temperature and humidity of the upper atmosphere. The increased contrast in atmospheric temperatures results in the subtropical jet stream moving south. Weather systems are now guided by the jet stream across southern California and the southeastern United States. In the United States, winters are warmer in the north central states and cooler in the Southeast and the Southwest. In India, South Africa, Australia, and Southeast Asia, the deceased amount of warm water results in less evaporation and less precipitation or drought.

On a positive note, the southerly jet stream breaks up tropical depressions as they move across the Atlantic, resulting in far fewer hurricanes during El Niño years.

After the warm waters of the western Pacific move east, conditions are slowly balanced out and conditions return to normal. Sometimes the conditions continue to change, resulting in colder than normal water off the coast of South America. This results in the condition know as La Niña, Spanish for "The Little Girl." The climatic impacts of La Niña tend to be the opposite of El Niño and are generally less pronounced. The subtropical jet stream moves farther north. The winter temperatures are warmer than normal in the Southeast and cooler than normal in the Northwest. Australia and Southeast Asia receive more rain than normal.

CAPT Review Questions 5-6

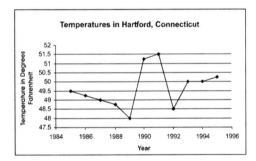
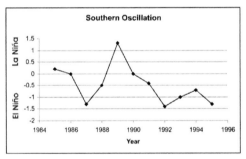

Figures 10-3. A and B. Accompany Review Questions 5-6

5. Graph A shows the fluctuation in yearly temperature that has occurred in Connecticut since 1985. Graph B shows the frequency of El Niño and La Niña events. The El Niño event that occurred in 1990 caused

    a. a decrease in temperature in Connecticut
    b. an increase in temperature in Connecticut
    c. a decrease in the amount of rainfall in Connecticut
    d. an increase in the amount of rainfall in Connecticut

6. Based on graphs A and B, this fluctuation in Connecticut's average temperature is caused by the
   a. concentration of chlorofluorocarbons in the atmosphere
   b. increase in the amount of carbon dioxide in the atmosphere as a result of human activity
   c. changes in the air currents over the Pacific Ocean
   d. addition of chemicals like sulfur dioxide to the atmosphere.

Answers to Review Questions 5-6

5. **The correct answer is b.** The temperature graph is at a high point in 1990, clearly showing an increase in temperature, not a decrease. Neither graph deals with average rainfall.

6. **The correct answer is c.** El Niño is caused by changes in the air currents over the South Pacific. Chlorofluorocarbons in the atmosphere cause the hole in the ozone layer, not El Niño. The increase in the amount of carbon dioxide in our atmosphere causes global warming, not El Niño. The introduction of sulfur dioxide into the atmosphere causes acid rain, not El Niño.

How Are Global Warming and the Greenhouse Effect Defined?

El Niño and La Niña were occurring long before man had the ability to affect global weather. The ozone hole is almost entirely due to man's activities, but the level of mankind's involvement with **global warming** and the **greenhouse effect** are being debated in political and scientific circles. There is agreement that over the last 100 years, the Earth has been getting warmer, and that the burning of fossil fuels combined with deforestation has resulted in increased levels of carbon dioxide in the atmosphere. There is, however, disagreement about why and how the Earth is getting warmer.

The greenhouse effect was discovered in the 1800s when scientists found that certain gasses allowed visible light to pass through them, like glass panes on a greenhouse, but absorbed infrared or heat energy. They hypothesized that increases in the amount of these gasses in the atmosphere would result in the Earth heating up. Sunlight passing through the atmosphere strikes the Earth. The surface absorbs some of the radiation and slowly emits it as infrared or heat. The greenhouse gases, mainly water vapor (H_2O), carbon dioxide (CO_2), methane (CH_4), and nitrous oxide (N_2O) absorb the radiation. They retain the energy and eventually re-emit it in all directions, including back toward the ground. As a result heat energy is trapped near the Earth's surface. One result is that the Earth has temperatures suitable for life as we know it. If the Earth had no greenhouse gasses, our average temperature would be a frigid $-18°C$ ($-32°F$). Earth would most likely be frozen from pole to pole.

The debate over the greenhouse effect concentrates on what the effects of increasing levels of carbon dioxide in the atmosphere are on global warming. It is known that there has been a steady increase in carbon dioxide levels for over 200 years and that the Earth's temperature has been increasing for 100 years. However, the Earth may still be in a natural warming cycle, and burning fossil fuel may have effects other than the increased levels of carbon dioxide.

How Can Changes in the Earth's Albedo Influence the Changes in Climate?

Albedo, a measure of how much light is reflected from a surface, may have a major impact on the climate. The following chart summarizes what happens to sunlight hitting the Earth today.

6% scattered by atmosphere
4% reflected from surface
19% absorbed by clouds and atmosphere
20% reflected by clouds
52% absorbed by surface

As the Earth gets warmer, glaciers melt, resulting in more exposed ground and ocean. Ice strongly reflects sunlight, and the ground and water absorb it. Therefore, the surface of the Earth and the air would become warmer. More glaciers would melt. However, if it is warmer then more water would evaporate, with increased humidity in the atmosphere, so there would be more clouds. Clouds reflect sunlight, preventing it from hitting the surface. Thus, the ground would not heat up as much. The clouds are composed of water vapor and water droplets, which absorb heat. Thus, they may be warming air higher in the atmosphere and re-emit heat radiation back toward the ground so that it does not cool off as quickly. The burning of fossil fuel releases carbon dioxide and water vapor, greenhouse gasses. However, the burning of coal and oil also releases smoke particles into the atmosphere, which scatter sunlight in the atmosphere before it hits the Earth. Man produces large amounts of carbon dioxide and other gasses such as methane. However, so does nature. Volcanic eruptions release carbon dioxide. Rotting vegetation releases methane.

What Might Be the Effects of Global Warming?

If the Earth continues to heat up over the next 100 years, sea levels could rise as much a meter due to melting glaciers and the fact that water expands as it gets warmer. This would result in the flooding of low-lying coastal areas. The increased difference in temperatures between temperate and polar zones would mean an increased number of severe storms. Some areas would receive more rain, while others would become arid. Major areas of food production would shift. There would be a dramatic effect on human health. Increased humidity, temperature, and carbon dioxide would lead to increased plant and fungus growth. The results would be increased allergies and fungal infections. Heat stress would be more common. It is estimated that the percentage of the world's population that live in tropical disease-infested regions will grow in area from 45%–60%. With the melting of the Arctic Ocean ice pack, the Polar easterlies, instead of being dry would become moist. During the winter, northern Canada and Russia would start to receive so much snow that it would not all melt during the summer. The result would be the building of snow packs, which lead to glaciers, which could start the next major ice age. Global warming could lead to a new ice age!

Chapter 11:
Earth History and Dynamics

The Earth

The third rock from the sun, the Earth, is not solid rock. From the time it formed, it has been slowly sorting itself into a core, mantle, and crust. Denser minerals have been sinking toward the center, lighter minerals rise to the surface. The differences in density and temperature between the layers result in processes that move and shape the surface of the Earth.

Why Is the Earth's Core Divided into an Inner and Outer Core?

At the center of the Earth is the **core**. It has a diameter of 5160 km, which is slightly less than half Earth's diameter of 12,756 km. It is composed primarily of very hot (6000°C) iron, with some small amounts of other metals mixed in. The core itself is divided into the inner and outer core. The inner core is 2680 km in diameter (radius of 1340 km). There, the pressure is so great that the iron is compressed from the molten state back into a crystalline solid. The outer core, 2190 km thick, is composed of molten iron. There is no solid connection between the inner core and the upper layers (the mantle and crust); the inner core is able to rotate at slightly different speeds than the surface of the Earth.

Why Is the Mantle Not Quite Rigid?

Above the core and below the crust is the **mantle**. It is composed of mostly dense, iron-rich minerals and is 2870 km thick. The mantle represents a little over half of the Earth's diameter. Under extreme pressure and high temperatures—6000°C at the core to 2000°C near the crust—the mantle is not quite rigid. It flows very slowly, at rates measured in millimeters per decade. Seismic studies indicate that there are great masses of hotter materials moving toward the surface and cooler materials sinking back toward the core.

What Creates the Asthenosphere?

Between 100 and 400 km down, the temperature is high enough and the pressure is low enough that a separate layer forms. In this layer, called the **asthenosphere**, mantle material can flow in convection currents with speeds of **centimeters** per year. Above the asthenosphere, the temperatures are too low for the minerals to actually flow; so they behave much like rocks in the lower crust. This layer, the uppermost mantle and the crust, is called the **lithosphere**.

Why Can Continental Crust Be Compared to an Iceberg?

When we stand outside, we are on the continental crust, a layer 32-70 km in thick and composed of silica-rich rocks, like granite. Its density is low enough, 2.8 g/cm^3 compared with the upper mantle's 3.3 g/cm^3, that its buoyancy keeps it from sinking back down into the mantle. Like an iceberg floating in the ocean, the higher the surface of the crust, the deeper into the mantle it also sinks. The deepest crust will be found below the highest mountains.

Why Can Oceanic Crust Be Recycled into the Mantle?

The **ocean crust** is mostly iron-rich rocks like basaltic and is very similar to the rocks found in the mantle. The oceanic crust is much thinner than the **continental crust**; it varies from only 5-10 km thick. It is dense enough, at 2.9 g/cm^3, that it can be forced back down into the mantle.

CAPT Review Questions 1-2

If you were to take the planet Earth and cut it in half like an orange, the inside would look like the picture below.

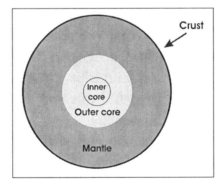

Figure 11-1. Accompanies Review Questions 1-2

1. The layer of the Earth that we can observe directly and know the most about is the
   a. inner core
   b. outer core
   c. mantle
   d. crust

2. The Earth has different layers because
   a. the Earth was exposed to different materials at different points in its formation, and layers were formed as these materials became part of the Earth
   b. early in its formation, the Earth was molten, and the materials from which it was made separated based on their densities
   c. it is very hot in the inner core, and some materials cannot be that hot
   d. some materials in the Earth are under high pressure so they move toward the Earth's center.

Answers to Review Questions 1-2

1. **The correct answer is d.** We can directly observe the crust and we have collected a great deal of information about how it works. We cannot directly observe the inner core, outer core, or mantel, so we have only limited information about them.

2. **The correct answer is b.** When the Earth formed, it was originally molten, and in that liquid state, all of its materials sorted themselves with the densest materials sinking to the middle of the Earth and the less dense materials floating on top of the more dense layers. The amount of additional material the Earth has acquired since its formation has been relatively small and could not account for such large layers of materials. The inner core is only 6000°C, and most materials would be able to exist at that temperature in either their liquid, gaseous, or plasma phase. The pressure at the Earth's center does not drive movement between layers.

Plate Tectonics

What Is the Theory of Plate Tectonics?

The **Theory of Plate Tectonics** states that Earth's lithosphere is broken into approximately 30 large sections called plates. These plates are pushed and pulled along by currents in the asthenosphere. Where the crust has cracked and the plates are moving apart, it is called a **divergent plate boundary**. Where two plates are colliding with each other, it is a **convergent plate boundary**, and where they are sliding past each other or are moving in the same direction but at different speeds it is called a **transform plate boundary**.

How Can You Recognize Divergent Plate Boundaries?

Divergent plate boundaries are created when convection currents in the asthenosphere approach the Earth's surface and are forced to flow off to the sides. These currents can literally rip the crust apart. Near the surface, the mantle material melts, creating **magma**. The magma works its way up through cracks in the crust and may erupt onto the surface, creating new crust. The rising convection currents, combined with the pressure from the magma, push the crust up into undersea mountain ranges known as mid-ocean ridges. The mid-ocean ridges are an area of constant seismic activity, but because the plates are separating, not grinding together, the earthquakes tend to be small. Characteristic features of divergent plate boundaries are **rift valleys**. They are long narrow valleys that form between fault lines or cracks between the diverging plates.

It is much easier to rip apart the 5–10 km thick oceanic crust than the 30–72 km thick continental crust. If a continent lies over the upwelling portion of convection current, the crust will rise, crack, and form fault-block mountains. If the continent stays there long enough, a rift valley may form. Eventually, the continent may completely split, creating a linier sea, like the Red Sea, which separates Asia and Africa.

How Is Crust Destroyed in a Subduction Zone?

As new crust is created at divergent plate boundaries, it is destroyed at convergent plate boundaries. If one of the plates has ocean crust on its leading edge and it runs up against a plate with continental crust, the denser oceanic crust is forced to bend down and be subducted under the continental crust. As it bends down, it will create a trench. The trench marks the start of a region we call the **subduction zone**. As the old ocean plate moves down into the asthenosphere it grinds against the continental plate. The friction of the collision raises the temperature, and the plate begins to melt. Blobs of magma rise from the subduction zone, cracking and melting their way through the crust. If they make it to the surface they will form volcanoes.

How May Convergent Plate Boundaries Create New Land?

If the oceanic plate contains islands, they may collide with and stick to the edge of the continent, increasing its size. The leading edge of the continental plate is under tremendous pressure, and its rocks may fracture and fold, creating folded mountains. The leading edge of the subducting plate melts back into the mantle. If the colliding plates both have oceanic crust on them, one of them slides under the other. A subduction zone forms with a trench, but instead of mountains on the upper plate, volcanoes grow from the ocean floor. The islands typically follow a curved path along the trench and are called an island arc. If the continental crust collides with continental crust, neither is able to subduct. In response to the heat and pressure, the land folds and faults to form the greatest mountain ranges on Earth. It is possible that oceanic crust can slide under continental crust and not subduct. When that happens, the crust may rise without folding or faulting. This is one way plateaus may form. Areas where plates collide have frequent severe earthquakes. The crust may not be moving very fast, but it has tremendous momentum.

How Are Transform Fault Boundaries Different from Convergent and Divergent Plate Boundaries?

America's most famous **fault line**, the San Andreas fault, represents a transform fault boundary. Along the San Andreas fault, the Pacific Plate is sliding roughly northwest at a little faster rate than the rest of North America. At irregular areas of the fault, pressure may build up until the crust snaps in a major earthquake. Along most transform faults, it is fairly easy for the crust to move. As a result, numerous small earthquakes are the norm. The mid-ocean ridges are crossed by thousands of transform faults that are the result of slight differences in the rate at which the sea floor spreads.

CAPT Review Question 3-5

Below is a picture of two pieces of the Earth's crust. The arrows indicate the direction of motion along the edge of each piece.

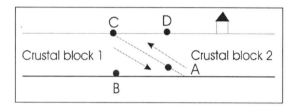

Figure 11-2. Accompanies Review Question 3-4

3. If the two pieces of crust in the picture above were to suddenly move
   a. a tsunami would most likely occur at point B
   b. a volcano would form at point D
   c. a mountain would form at point C
   d. an earthquake would occur at point A

4. The feature found at point C is would most likely be a
   a. ridge
   b. trench
   c. fault
   d. rift valley

5. If an aerial view of point C before the two pieces of crust moved looked like the picture below,

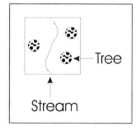

Figure 11-3. Accompanies First Part of Review Question 5

which of the pictures below best represents what point C would look like after the two pieces of crust moved?

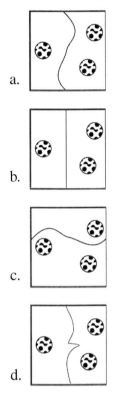

a.

b.

c.

d.

Answers to Review Questions 3-5

3. **The correct answer is d.** When pieces of the crust move, earthquakes occur. Tsunami's generally only occur when an earthquake happens underwater along a coastline. Since there is no water or coastline in the picture, it is unlikely there will be a tsunami. Volcanoes do not form along fault lines. While mountains can form along fault lines, the process takes millions of years and would not occur as the result of a single crustal movement.

4. **The correct answer is c.** Faults form when plates scrape past or move along each other. Ridges, trenches, and rift valleys form when two plates are moving away from each other, not along each other.

5. **The correct answer is d.** Earthquakes disrupt the streambed of a river causing the river's course to be slightly offset. An earthquake would not cause a stream to become straighter or cause the landscape to rotate 90°.

What Is the Relationship between Lava and Volcanoes, and Where They Are Found?

The type of volcano that forms depends on the kind of lava it erupts. The type of magma depends on where in the lithosphere it forms. The closer its composition is to mantle minerals, the hotter and more fluid it will be. The more crustal rocks and water that have been dissolved in it, the cooler and more explosive it will be. Mid-ocean hot spots, such as Hawaii, erupt hot fluid lava. If a volcano forms over the subduction zone, the lava will contain additional water and melted crust rocks. Eruptions can range from gentle lava flows to explosive eruptions. Mid-continental hot spots, such as Yellowstone Park, only erupt violently. They may be so explosive that they do not leave volcanoes.

The Rock Cycle

After reviewing this section, you should be able to answer the following questions:

What is the rock cycle?

Why is magma considered the mother of all rocks?

What is the difference between mechanical and chemical weathering?

How does mechanical weathering break rocks down?

How does chemical weathering change rock?

How are weathered sediments moved to new locations?

Why is gravity an important source of erosion?

How are sedimentary rocks formed?

What is the origin of metamorphic rocks?

What Is the Rock Cycle?

As soon as rocks form, outside forces start to act on them. Within the Earth, the temperatures and pressures may change their crystalline structure or composition. Water percolating through the rock may add or remove minerals. If the rocks are near the Earth's surface, oxygen, acid rain, fluctuating temperatures, and moisture affects them. The combination of processes that change rocks from one type to another and perhaps back again is called the **rock cycle**. It is the result of a combination of actions due to plate tectonics, weathering, erosion, deposition, and metamorphism.

Why Is Magma Considered the Mother of All Rocks?

The rock cycle starts with magma. The molten material may cool and slowly crystallize in the Earth or erupt onto the surface as lava to form igneous rocks. Intrusive igneous rocks form from magma crystallizing inside the Earth's crust, and extrusive igneous rocks form from lava solidifying on Earth's surface.

What Is the Difference between Mechanical and Chemical Weathering?

If an igneous rock comes into contact with fresh magma, the rock may melt and start the rock cycle all over again. Early in the Earth's history, when the planet had only a thin crust of igneous rock, the rock cycle was simple. It went from magma to extrusive igneous rock, to melting, to magma, to extrusive igneous rock and so on, until the first day that rain hit the ground. Then weathering and erosion broke down the rocks and minerals. Breakdown of rocks occurs by **mechanical weathering**, which is the physical breakdown of the rock, or by **chemical weathering**, which results in changes in the composition of the rock.

How Does Mechanical Weathering Break Rocks Down?

Mechanical weathering results in smaller fragments of the original rock. In Connecticut, as in most areas with cold winters, ice wedging is an important means of mechanical weathering. Liquid water may seep into, or collect within pores or cracks in a rock. When the temperature drops below freezing, the water within the rock freezes and expands. The expansion forces fragments off the surface of the rock or may widen a crack within the rock. As the crack widens, it is easier for more water to get in, which if it freezes, creates an even larger crack.

Most rocks were formed under great pressure deep within the crust. If, through erosion and uplift, they become exposed on the surface, they may expand and crack. In the process of exfoliation, rocks may actually look like they are peeling. Once rocks crack, they have an opening into which roots can grow. As the root grows, it forces the rock even further apart.

Abrasion occurs wherever rocks or rock particles are forced to strike other rocks. Wind may pick up sand and blast it against exposed rock. In fast-moving streams, water may tumble rocks downstream. As the rocks bang against each other, they knock off fragments. At the beach, as waves pound our rocky coastlines; they pick up and tumble the stones back and forth, creating sand. As glaciers move down through valleys or across the continent, rocks become embedded in the ice like grit on sandpaper. As the glacier moves across the land, these now ice-bound rocks grind away at the bedrock beneath the glaciers. Landslides, where perhaps hundreds of tons of rocks come bounding and smashing down a mountainside, are a major source of abrasion for the rocks in the landslide as well as anything into which they run.

How Does Chemical Weathering Change Rock?

Chemical weathering results in a change in the composition of a rock. Generally this makes the rock softer and thus more water soluble or susceptible to mechanical weathering. In chemical weathering, chemical reactions occur between the minerals in the rocks and water, oxygen, or other chemicals found in the air. The chemical reaction results in the formation of new minerals or the release of dissolved substances. For example, limestone and marble are made from the mineral calcite, $CaCO_3$. When carbonic acid, H_2CO_3 (which is made from dissolving carbon dioxide, CO_2, in water, H_2O) comes into contact with calcite, it dissolves the calcite. In chemical weathering, water may also chemically combine with a mineral. Very fine clays may be the result of water reacting with the mineral feldspar. Many minerals containing iron oxidize to form iron oxides, commonly referred to as rust. The reddish color of many rocks and minerals is the result of oxidation. Generally, the warmer and moister the climate, the more rapid the chemical weathering occurs.

How Are Weathered Sediments Moved to New Locations?

Erosion is the process of moving weathered pieces of rock to new locations. Agents of erosion include moving water in streams and waves at the beach, glaciers, wind, and gravity as in landslides and soil creep. **Gravity** is the driving force behind all agents of erosion. With the exception of the Polar regions, moving liquid water is the major mover of Earth's materials. In mountains or hills, where you find rapids and waterfalls, even large rocks can move along riverbeds. Every time it rains, drops hitting exposed soil will splatter particles in all directions. Water flowing over the ground from a heavy rain can move fine sediment down hill to collect into drainage channels or brooks. Through successively larger streams, sediments will eventually be dumped into a lake or the ocean. There, the sediments may finally settle to the bottom. The wind is an important agent of erosion in arid regions or where there is no vegetation to protect the dirt or soil. Even the strongest wind, however, can only move the finest rock particles. Eventually, the wind just leaves the coarser sands and stones behind. When it does rain in the desert, there is nothing to stop flash floods from carrying large amounts of sediment across the land. In Polar regions or at high altitudes glaciers act like rivers of ice. Rocks or landslides, which may fall onto the glacier as it grinds down through a valley, may be carried for many miles before being dumped at the head of the glacier, where the ice melts or breaks off into the sea. There is no limit to the size of the rocks a glacier may carry.

CAPT Review Questions 6-7

Below is a graph that shows how slow a river needs to be moving in order to drop the sediments it is carrying.

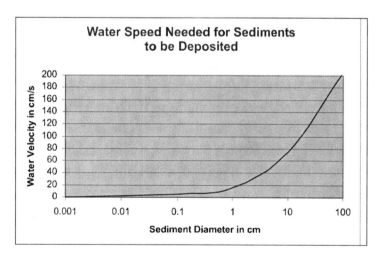

Figure 11-4. Accompanies Review Questions 6-7

6. In a lake or other body of water where there is little or no current, you would expect to find sediments in the water that are
   a. 0.01 cm in diameter
   b. 0.1 cm in diameter
   c. 1 cm in diameter
   d. 10 cm in diameter

Type of Rock	Sediment size
Conglomerate	0.1–100 cm
Sandstone	0.01–0.1 cm
Shale	0–0.01 cm

7. The type of sedimentary rock that is most likely to form at the bottom of the lake is
   a. conglomerate
   b. sandstone
   c. shale

Answers to CAPT Review Questions 6-7

6. **The correct answer is a.** The water speed in a lake is close to zero, and sediments that are 0.01 cm in diameter or smaller are not deposited at a water speed of zero. Sediments that are 0.1 cm in diameter are deposited when the water speed drops to about 2 cm/s. Sediments that are 1 cm in diameter are deposited when the water speed drops below 12 cm/s. Sediments that are 10 cm in diameter are deposited when the water speed drops below 70 cm/s.

7. **The correct answer is c.** Shale forms from very small sediments (0-0.01 cm) which are only deposited in still water or water with a velocity of zero, like lake or deep ocean water. Conglomerates are formed from sediments that are between 0.1 and 100 cm in diameter. Since the water velocity in a lake is close to zero, those sediments were deposited before the water ever reached the lake. Sandstone is formed from sediments that are between 0.01 and 0.1 cm in diameter. Since those sediments are deposited at water speeds higher then zero, they were deposited before the water reached the lake.

Why Is Gravity an Important Source of Erosion?

Without gravity, nothing moves downhill. Mass movement is the downslope movement of Earth materials as the result of the force of gravity. Even very gentle hillsides may experience creep. Creep is the very slow mass movement of soil down a gentle slope. Much more dramatic than creep are landslides. These are rapid falls or rock and soil down unstable slopes. If there is a source of water, landslides may turn into mudflows and carry great amounts of sediment, at high speed, for many kilometers.

How Are Sedimentary Rocks Formed?

Once there is not enough energy to continue moving sediment, it is deposited. If enough material builds up, sedimentary rocks may be formed. Sedimentary rocks are formed when **sediments** are lithified into rock by the processes of **compaction** or **cementation**.

Sedimentary rocks are formed when the grains of the sediment are compressed by overlying sediment or the grains are held together by mineral cement such as calcite or silica. As pressure builds, the grains in the sediment are forced closer together. Coarse grains may become interlocked. Water is constantly percolating through the sediment, carrying minerals dissolved from the soil or other rocks. The minerals may precipitate out, cementing the grains together.

There are three main groups of sedimentary rocks: clastic, chemical, and organic. **Clastic sedimentary rocks** are formed from fragments of weathered and eroded older rocks. An example, sandstone is composed of sand grains—the same as you would find in sand dunes or beach deposits. **Chemical sedimentary rocks** are formed from minerals dissolved from rocks or sediment and then precipitated from water. Most limestone is actually made from calcite, which is deposited on the ocean floor from the mineral dissolved in sea water. **Organic sedimentary rocks** are formed from the remains of once-living things. Chalk is a type of limestone, but the calcite is from the shells of billions of microscopic animals. Most coal is formed from the remains of plants that grew in great swamps around 350 million years ago.

Like igneous rocks, sedimentary rocks are also subject to weathering and erosion. If they come into contact with magma, they may melt.

What Is the Origin of Metamorphic Rocks?

Once igneous or sedimentary rocks form, they may never make it to the surface, but may just keep getting buried deeper and deeper. When this happens, the pressure on them continues to build, and the temperature continues to rise. The rise in temperature may initiate physical and chemical reactions within the rock, creating the third group of rocks, the **metamorphic rocks**.

Regional metamorphism occurs near convergent plate boundaries. The pressure and heat generated from two plates colliding deforms and transforms the rocks in the area. Today, deep beneath the Andes or Himalayan Mountains, metamorphic rocks are being created. Everywhere there are mountain ranges, there are metamorphic rocks deep below the surface. Higher in the crust or away from the plate boundary, you may get contact metamorphism. Rising magma or thick lava flows can heat nearby rocks, melting or altering some of the minerals in them. The melted minerals may, in turn, react with surrounding rocks. In addition, the water in a rock that may be under great pressure, may become super heated and thus may be able to dissolve minerals not possible near the surface. If these super hot, mineral-rich waters cool in cracks in the rock, they will deposit their load, creating veins of minerals. If the water makes it to the surface in the form of hot springs or geysers, the minerals will be deposited on the surface.

Once a metamorphic rock is formed, it is not immune to changes from temperature, pressure, chemical reaction. It may melt back into magma, or it may be further metamorphosed. If eventually, through uplift and erosion, it makes it to the surface, it will be subject to weathering and erosion.

CAPT Review Questions 8-9

Below is a diagram showing how one type of rock can change into another type of rock.

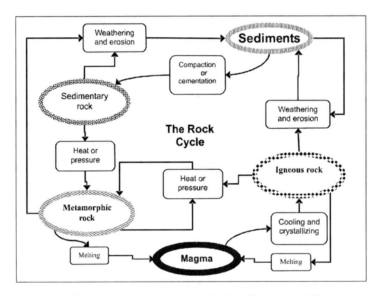

Figure 11-5. Accompanies Review Questions 8-9

8. June was out in her backyard one day and found a piece of slate, a metamorphic rock. Knowing that slate is metamorphic, June can also say that her rock formed as a result of
   a. melting and cooling
   b. heat and pressure
   c. weathering and erosion
   d. compaction and cementation

9. If June left her rock outside, over time her rock would
   a. weather and form sediments
   b. melt and form magma
   c. cool and form an igneous rock
   d. heat up and form a metamorphic rock

Answers to Review Questions 8-9

8. **The correct answer is b.** Heat and pressure forms metamorphic rocks like June's. Melting and cooling form igneous rocks. Weathering and erosion form sediments, which then go on to form sedimentary rocks. Compaction and cementation turn sediments into sedimentary rocks.

9. **The correct answer is a.** Rocks that are exposed on the Earth's surface are weathered by wind, water, and ice to form sediments. Being exposed on the Earth's surface will not cause a rock to melt and form magma. In order to cool and form an igneous rock, the original rock would have to be melted into magma, which does not happen to rocks that are sitting exposed on the Earth's surface. The temperatures and pressures necessary to metamorphose a rock do not occur on the Earth's surface unless they are near a volcano.

Why Are Index Fossils Important?

Sedimentary rocks can be identified by their type of sediment and what fossils are present. **Fossils** are often found preserved in sedimentary rocks. Their presence helps date the rocks and correlate them to rocks that may be separated by hundreds or even thousands of kilometers. Geologists found that the younger the rock layers, the more that their fossils were like modern animals and plants than fossils. As the rock layers become older, the greater the difference between the fossils and today's living organisms. Some fossils, referred to as **index fossils**, are very useful in matching up rock layers. Index fossils represent animals that lived only during a relatively short period of Earth's history but were very common over a wide area.

How Do Geologists Determine How Old Rocks Actually Are?

In the nineteenth century, geologists learned how to determine how old rocks were relative to each other, but it was not until the discovery of radioactivity that they were able to determine how old the rocks actually were. Many igneous and metamorphic rocks contain small amounts of the radioactive isotopes of the elements uranium, U-235, or potassium, K-40. The U-235 eventually decays into lead, Pb-207, and the K-40 into argon, Ar-40. By comparing how much of the original element there is with how much of the new element there is, scientists are able to determine the age of the rock. The time it takes half of the parent element to decay into the daughter element is called the half-life of the element. It takes 700 million years for half of a sample of U-235 to decay into lead. It takes 8.4 billion years for half a sample of K-40 to decay into Ar-40. Living tissue contains small amounts of the radioactive isotope of carbon, C-14, which will decay into nitrogen-14, N-14. It has a half-life of only about 6000 years. Some problems arise when dating rocks or fossils that are only a few million years old. The half-life of C-14 is so short that after around 75,000 years there is not enough C-14 left to measure. If you try using U-235, not enough has turned into lead to find a ratio.

CAPT Review Questions 10-11

By studying the fossil remains of dogs found in rocks from the Cenazoic era and the amount of U-235 that had broken down into Pb-207, a geologist was able to put together the family tree below.

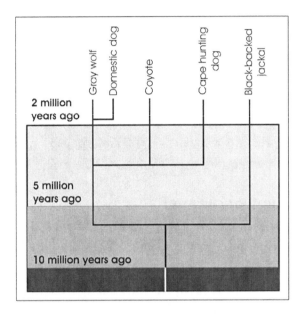

Figure 11-6. Accompanies Review Questions 10-11

10. Based on the relationships shown above, it is possible to infer that the rocks in which dog fossils are found contain
   a. large percentages of Pb-207
   b. small percentages of Pb-207
   c. small percentages of U-235
   d. neither Pb-207 nor U-235

11. Based on the graph above, it would be safe to conclude that rocks containing the remains of a coyote are about
   a. 20 million years old
   b. 10 million years old
   c. 5 million years old
   d. 2 million years old

Answers to CAPT Review Questions 10-11

10. **The correct answer is b.** The dog fossils are relatively young so very little of the U-235 has had time to break down into Pb-207. Small amounts of U-235 would indicate that a lot of time had passed, and the dog fossils are relatively young. If there had been no Pb-207 or U-235, they would not have been able to date the fossils and determine which animals came first.

11. **The correct answer is d.** Coyotes evolved between 3 and 4 million years ago, so a rock containing coyote remains could be about 2 million years old not 5, 10, or 20 million years old.

What Is the Geologic Column?

Using index fossils and the laws of superposition, horizontality, and the principals of uniformitarianism, geologists are able to determine the relative ages of rock layers around the world. Combining data from all the continents, they produced an ordered arrangement of Earth's rock layers, which we call the **geologic column**. It acts as a timeline of the Earth's history with the present at the top and the oldest known rocks at the bottom.

Early on, geologist noticed that there were relatively abrupt changes in the fossils found in the geologic column. The same group of animals may be present for millions of years, and then with the length of time it took a rock layer to form, they disappeared, only to be replaced by a new species. Sometimes the change in species could be due to changes in climate, the arrangement of the continents, or oceans, or some catastrophic events associated with asteroid or comet impacts or major volcanic eruptions.

Glossary of Terms

Abrasion: The type of mechanical weathering in which rocks collide and scrape against each other, wearing away the exposed surfaces.

Absolute age: The actual age of a rock or fossil.

Absolute magnitude: The actual brightness of a star as seen from 10 parsecs (32 light years) away is the absolute magnitude.

Absorption spectrum: A dark line spectrum, produced when light is filtered by a cool gas between the light source and the observer.

Absorption: Uptake of nutrients through the digestive tract

Acceleration: The rate of change of velocity with respect to time. The act of "speeding" up.

Acid: A compound containing hydrogen that ionizes to yield hydrogen ions (H^+) in water

Action potential: A nerve impulse; the electrical flow across neuron membranes

Adiabatic: The change in temperature of a mass of air due to its rising or sinking is known as adiabatic. The rising and expansion of air results in adiabatic cooling. The sinking and contraction of air results in adiabatic heating.

Aggregate: A deposit of rock fragments such as sand or gravel.

Air mass: A large body of air with uniform temperature and moisture content.

Albedo: The amount of sunlight reflected off a surface such as a cloud or the ground.

Alluvial fan: Fan-shaped deposits of sediments at the base of a slope on land.

Alveolus: Small sacs in the lungs where gas exchange occurs during respiration

Ampere: The metric unit of current, 1 coulomb per second

Amplitude: The height of a wave crest above the average value is the amplitude.

Anion: Any atom or group of atoms with a negative charge

Anthracite: The hardest form of coal and is almost pure carbon

Antibiotics: Used to combat infections created by bacteria, not effective against viruses

Apparent magnitude: The brightness of a star as it appears from Earth is the apparent magnitude.

Aqueduct: An artificial channel, conduit, or pipe for moving water from one place to another.

Aquifer: An underground layer of porous rock or soil that contains a large amount of groundwater.

Asteroid belt: The region between the orbits of Mars and Jupiter where most of the asteroids orbit.

Asteroid: A "minor planet" or chunk of rock or metal that orbits the sun. Although an asteroid is smaller than a planet, it is larger than a meteoroid.

Asthenosphere: The zone of the mantle just beneath the lithosphere that consists of slowly flowing solid rock.

Astronomical unit (AU): The average distance between the Earth and the sun is an astronomical unit. It is approximately 150 million km.

Atmospheric pressure: The ratio of the weight of the air to the area of the surface on which it presses

Atom: The smallest property of an element that retains the properties of that element

Atomic number: The number of protons in the nucleus of an atom of an element

Autumnal equinox: The first day of fall in the Northern Hemisphere. At noon, the sun is located directly over the equator. This typically occurs on September 23.

Axis: The imaginary line that passes through a planet's poles and around which it rotates is known as its axis.

Axon: A long extension of a neuron that transmits information

Barrier island: A long narrow island composed entirely of sand that generally lies parallel and close to shore. It is created by the shoreward migration of sand dunes along a coastline.

Base: A compound that ionizes to yield hydroxide ions (OH⁻) in water

Bedrock: The unweathered, solid, parent rock is called bedrock. It is the uppermost part of the solid crust of the Earth.

Berm: The raised portion of a beach located above the elevation of the high tide.

Bile: Digestive material produced by the liver and stored in the gallbladder, used to digest fat

Biogas: A gas that is generated by the decomposition of organic waste by bacteria, a mixture of methane, and carbon dioxide.

Biomass fuel: A power source made from things that were once living; for example, fuel that is created from plants.

Biome: A large geographical region characterized by climate, temperature, flora, fauna, and precipitation

Biotechnology: The application of science to solve practical problems

Bituminous coal: Soft coal that has a high percent of impurities; breakdown of rocks, minerals, and organic matter.

Blood cells: A part of the circulatory system; responsible for the transport of oxygen (red) and immune function (white)

Brain: A complex collection of neurons that is found in the skull

Breeze: A gentle wind that extends over a distance of less than 100 km.

Cation: Any atom or group of atoms with a positive charge

Cell wall: Found in plant cells as well as bacteria cells, gives the cell a rigid shape

Cell: The basic unit of life

Cementation: The process in which dissolved minerals left behind by water passing through sediments glue the sediments together.

Cenozoic era: The Cenozoic era of geologic history started 66 million years ago; it is the era in which we live and is commonly called the Age of Mammals.

Centrioles: Exist as a pair in the cell; function in cellular division; made up of microfilaments

Centripetal force: Centripetal force is the force needed to keep an object in a circular path.

Cepheid variable: A type of star that oscillates in brightness in periods ranging from 1 to about 100 days. There is a measured relationship between the absolute magnitude of these stars and their period of oscillation, which allow us to determine their distance from Earth.

Channel: The path a stream follows.

Chemical property: The ability of a substance to undergo chemical reactions and to form new substances

Chemical reaction: The changing of substances to other substances by the breaking of old bonds and the formation of new bonds

Chlorofluorocarbons: Chlorine compounds formerly used in air conditioners, refrigerators, and spray cans; they are also called CFCs.

Chloroplast: The organelle found in organisms that go through the process of photosynthesis, contains chlorophyll

Chromosomes: A condensed bundle of chromatin visible during cell division; contains the DNA of the cell

Chromosphere: The lower, reddish, relatively thin part of the sun's atmosphere above the photosphere but below the corona is known as the chromosphere.

Circuit, parallel: An electrical circuit in which devices are placed directly across the voltage source or line. There are as many separate paths for current flow as there are branches in the circuit.

Circuit, series: An electrical circuit in which devices are placed directly one after another along the voltage source or line. There is a single path for current flow in the circuit.

Circuit: Pathways along conductors that electrons move to produce various effects, depending on the devices present in the circuit

Clastic sedimentary rock: Rock that is made up of fragments from preexisting rocks.

Climate: The general weather conditions for an area as measured over many years is the climate.

Climatology: The study of the Earth's climate in order to understand and predict climatic change, based on past and present variations in temperature, precipitation, wind, and other weather variables.

Clone: A genetically identical copy of a cell or individual

Cold front: A cold front is a boundary formed where a cold air mass overtakes and lifts a warm air mass.

Combination reaction: A chemical change in which two or more substances react to form a single new substance; also called a synthesis reaction

Combustion reaction: A chemical change in which oxygen reacts with another substance, often producing energy in the form of heat and light

Comet: A comet is an object that orbits the sun in very elongated elliptical orbits and is composed of ice and dust.

Compaction: The process of squeezing the water and air out of sediments.

Compound: A substance that can be separated into simpler substances (elements or other compounds) only by chemical reactions

Condensation nuclei: The solid particles in the atmosphere, such as ice and dust, which provide the surfaces on which water vapor condenses.

Condensation: A process by which water vapor changes to liquid water is known as condensation.

Conduction: The type of energy transfer in which vibrating molecules pass heat along to other vibrating molecules by direct contact.

Conductor: A material through which electricity passes freely, that is, the material offers minimal resistance to the movement of electrons

Conservation: The reduction in the amount of material used.

Continental ice sheet: A mass of ice that covers a large land area.

Continuous spectrum: A spectrum of all radiation at all wavelengths but with neither absorption nor emission lines.

Contour interval: The difference in elevation between one contour line and the next on a topographical map.

Contour line: A line on a map connecting points with the same elevation.

Convergent plate boundary: An area in which two of the Earth's lithospheric plates are colliding.

Core: The center of a planetary body.

Coriolis effect: The deflection of wind and ocean currents caused by the Earth's rotation.

Corona: The outermost and faintest part of the sun's atmosphere is known as the corona. It is composed of plasma that is millions of degrees Celsius.

Coulomb: The unit of electrical charge

Covalent bond: A chemical bond resulting from the sharing of valence electron pairs between two atoms. One shared pair of electrons is a single covalent bond, two shared pairs of electrons is a double covalent bond, and three shared pairs of electrons is a triple covalent bond.

Cross-cutting: The principle stating that a fault or intrusion is younger than the rock it cuts across.

Crude oil: Unrefined petroleum; the oil that is pumped out of the ground.

Crust: The thin outermost layer of the solid Earth.

Current: The flow of electrons in an electric circuit from negative to positive

Cytoplasm: A gel like substance within the cell in which most of the organelles reside

Decomposers: Organisms that breakdown organic matter into its component nutrients

Decomposition reaction: A chemical change in which a single compound is broken down into two or more simpler products

Deflation hollow: A shallow bowl-like depression left after wind has eroded a layer of exposed soil.

Deforestation: The removal of all the trees from a forested area without replanting. It may result in the loss of topsoil and water pollution.

Delta: A delta is the fan-shaped deposit of sediment at the mouth of a stream.

Density dependent limiting factors: Factors that limit a population only when a population reaches a certain density (mice neglect their young when overcrowding is an issue)

Density independent limiting factors: Factors that affect all populations regardless of the density

Density: The ratio of a mass of an object to its volume

Deoxyribonucleic acid (DNA): A double stranded nucleic acid that contains the sugar deoxyribose; codes for the information that controls the proteins produced in an organism; transfers inherited information from one generation to the next

Deposition: Deposition occurs when sediments are laid down on the ground or sink to the bottom of a body of water.

Desalination: The process of creating freshwater from salt water by removing the salt from ocean water.

Desert pavement: A surface composed of closely backed stones that are left after the wind has removed all the finer particles.

Desertification: The process by which productive semiarid farm or grassland becomes desert.

Dew point: The temperature at which air must be cooled to become saturated.

Diatomic: A molecule containing two atoms covalently bonded

Diffusion: A passive form of transport across a semi-permeable membrane; the direction of movement is from higher concentration to lower concentration

Diploid: A cell having two sets of chromosomes, one inherited from each parent

Disconformity: The boundary between layers of rock that have not been deposited continuously.

Divergent plate boundary: An area in which two of Earth's lithospheric plates are pulling apart.

Doppler effect: An apparent shift in the wavelength of sound or light emitted by a source moving away (wavelengths are lengthened) or toward (wavelengths are shortened) an observer.

Drumlin: A long, low, teardrop-shaped hill formed when a glacier moves over existing moraine.

Dune: A mound of wind-blown sand.

Earthquake: A vibration of the Earth's crust.

Ecosystem: All of the organisms and abiotic factors occupying a defined area at a given time

El Niño: A warm ocean current that develops off the western coast of South America and can cause short-term climatic changes felt worldwide.

Electricity: The flow of electrons along a conductor

Electromagnetic radiation: Any radiation that results from changing electric or magnetic fields. The electromagnetic spectrum is all electromagnetic radiations from the longest waved radio waves to the shortest waved gamma rays.

Electron: A negatively charged subatomic particle

Element: A substance that cannot be changed into a simpler substance under normal laboratory conditions

Elevation: The height above mean sea level.

Ellipse: A closed curve drawn about two points (foci) so that the sum of the distance from the line to the two foci remains constant. It looks like a slightly oval circle.

EM spectrum: A series of energy waves that travel in a vacuum at a speed of 3.0×10^{10} cm/s; includes radio waves, microwaves, visible light, infrared and ultraviolet light, x-rays, and gamma rays

Emission spectrum: A bright line spectrum, generally created by a glowing gas under low pressure.

Endoplasmic Reticulum(ER): A series of connected membranes within the cell that produce, transport, and store secretory proteins

Endothermic reaction: A chemical change in which energy is absorbed; the energy content of the products is higher than the energy content of the reactants.

Epoch: A subdivision of a geologic period.

Era: The largest unit of geologic time.

Erosion: The process by which sediments are transported.

Esker: A long winding ridge of gravel formed from sediment deposited in a stream flowing through a crevice in a glacier or an ice cave under the glacier.

Eukaryotic cells: Cells that contain a membrane-bound nucleus and organelles; DNA is organized into discrete chromosomes housed in the nucleus

Evaporates: Sediments left behind after water evaporates are called evaporates.

Evaporation: The process by which liquid water changes to water vapor.

Evolution: Changes in the genetic make-up of a living population over time

Exfoliation: A process in which sheets of rock peel or flake off as a result of weathering.

Exothermic reaction: A chemical change in which energy is released in the form of heat; the energy content of the products is less than the energy content of the reactants.

Extrusive igneous rock: Rocks formed from lava that hardens on the Earth's surface.

Facilitated diffusion: A passive form of diffusion across a cell membrane made possible by the assistance of the membrane bound proteins

Fault: A break or fracture in the Earth's crust along which rocks on either side move.

Fertilization: The joining of haploid gametes in sexual reproduction

Floodplain: Part of a valley floor that may be covered with water when the stream running through it floods.

Fluid mosaic model (cell membrane): A model of the cell membrane that depicts the structure as a lipid bi-layer (2 layers) with proteins dispersed throughout and spanning the entire two layers

Focus: One of the points about which an ellipse is drawn. The center of the sun is one focus of Earth's elliptical orbit.

Force: A push or pull acting on an object. The unit of force in the metric system is a newton; 1 newton of net force acting on an object of 1 kilogram will cause the object to accelerate at a rate of 1 meter per second each second.

Fossil fuel: A nonrenewable energy resource formed over thousands to hundreds of millions of years from the compression and partial decomposition of plants and single-cell organisms.

Fossil: The trace or remains of a plant or animal in sedimentary rock or ancient sediment.

Frequency: The number of waves that pass a particular point each second; the shorter the wavelength the greater the frequency of the electromagnetic radiation.

Front: The boundary between two air masses of different densities is known as a front.

Fusion: The combination, under extreme heat and pressure, of lighter atomic nuclei to form heavier nuclei. It is accompanied by the release of energy.

Gasohol: A fuel that is a combination of gasoline and alcohol ethanol.

Gene: The unit of hereditary material that controls the traits of a particular organism; located on the chromosomes

Genotype: An individual's genetic makeup

Geologic column: An arrangement of rock layers based on the ages of the rocks.

Geothermal energy: Power produced from heating water with the heat from hot gasses, rock, or magma within the Earth.

Glacier: A mass of moving ice on the Earth's surface.

Global warming: A rise in global temperatures that may be due to increases in atmospheric carbon dioxide from deforestation and burning of fossil fuels; this phenomenon is related to the greenhouse effect.

Golgi body: A series of flattened membranes that store, modify, and transport secretory proteins

Gravity: The force of attraction between two objects. The strength of the attraction is proportional to the mass of the objects and is inversely proportional to the square of the distance between them.

Gravity: The term given for the attraction between objects having mass

Greenhouse effect: The process by which the atmosphere traps infrared rays over the Earth's surface.

Groundwater depletion: The removal of water from an aquifer faster than it can be replaced is known as groundwater depletion.

Group: A vertical column of elements in the periodic table; the constituent elements of a group have similar chemical and physical properties.

Hachure: The short line at a right angle to a contour line; it indicates a depression. The hachures point in the direction of the depression.

Haploid: A cell or gamete having one complete set of chromosomes

Headland: An erosion-resistant projection of rock that sticks out from the shoreline into the ocean is known as a headland.

Heat energy: The energy that is transferred from one body to another because of a temperature difference. Heat energy always transfers from the warmer body to the cooler body.

Heterogeneous: A mixture that is not uniform in composition; its components are readily distinguished.

Homogeneous: A mixture that is completely uniform in composition; its components are not distinguishable.

Homologous: Having characteristics that are similar because they were inherited from a common ancestor

Hydrocarbon: Any compound made up of atoms of carbon and hydrogen.

Hydroelectric energy: The power produced by running water.

Ice age: A long period of climatic cooling in which ice sheets covered large portions of the Earth's land surface.

Index contour: Every fifth, darkened, contour line on a topographical map. Index contours are often labeled with the elevation of the line.

Index fossil: A guide fossil; it is a common fossil found in the rock layers of only one geologic age and is used to establish the relative age of the rock layers.

Intrusive igneous rock: Rocks formed from the cooling of magma beneath the Earth's surface.

Ion: An atom or group of atoms that has a positive or negative charge; cations are ions with a positive charge, and anions are ions with a negative charge.

Ionic bond: The electrostatic attraction that binds oppositely charged ions together

Ionic compound: A compound composed of positive and negative ions

Irrigation: The supplying of land, especially farmland with water through means such as ditches or spraying.

Isobar: A line drawn on a weather map connecting points of equal atmospheric pressure.

Isopleth: A line that connect points of equal or constant value such as contour lines on a topographical map, connecting areas of equal pressure or temperature.

Isotope: An atom of the same element that has the same atomic number but different atomic masses due to a different number of neutrons

Jet streams: Bands of high-speed, high-altitude, westerly winds.

Jovian planet: Any of the first four outer planets that are similar to Jupiter in terms of their large size and gaseous composition.

Kettle: A depression in a glacial outwash plane that was created when a large block of ice was covered with sediment and later melted.

Kuiper Belt: The region of the solar system beyond Neptune, which may contain large ice and dust objects that are smaller than planets but larger than comets.

Kuiper Belt object: A large comet-like object that resembles Pluto or Neptune's moon, Triton.

La Niña: A very cold current that develops off the western coast of South America and can cause short-term climatic changes felt worldwide. Generally, these currents are the opposite of those caused by El Niño and are not as severe.

Latitude: The angular distance north or south of the equator.

Lava: Hot, molten rock on the Earth's surface.

Law of conservation of energy: Energy is neither created nor destroyed in an ordinary chemical or physical process.

Law of conservation of mass: Mass can be neither created nor destroyed in an ordinary chemical or physical process

Lever: A simple machine that magnifies the force applied to an object via a pivot point or fulcrum

Light-year (LY): A light-year is the distance that light (electromagnetic radiation) can travel in 1 year (approximately 9.5×10^{12} km = 9.5 trillion km).

Lithification: The process of turning to stone.

Lithosphere: The thin outer shell of the Earth, consisting of the crust and rigid portion of the upper mantle.

Loess: Thick, yellowish deposits of fine windblown sediments.

Longitude: The angular distance east or west of the prime meridian.

Lysosomes: Single-membrane sac-like organelles filled with enzymes

Magma: Hot, molten rock within the Earth's crust.

Magnetism: The ability to attract certain metals and their alloys, in particular, cobalt iron and nickel

Magnitude: The amount of energy released in an earthquake.

Mantle: The layer of the Earth beneath the crust and above the core. It is composed of dense, iron-rich minerals.

Map legend: A map insert that contains the meaning of the symbols used on the map.

Map scale: An insert that gives the ratio or a graphic depiction of distance on the Earth compared to the distance shown on the map.

Mass number: The total number of protons and neutrons in the nucleus of an atom

Mass: The amount of matter that an object contains; the System International (SI) base unit of mass is the kilogram

Matter: Anything that takes up space and has mass

Mean sea level: The average elevation between high and low tide.

Mechanical energy: The energy an object possesses because of its motion or position

Meiosis: A form of cell division that reduces the number of chromosomes by half that takes place when the mature eggs and sperm are formed

Mesozoic era: The Mesozoic era extends from 245 to 66 million years; it is commonly known as the Age of Dinosaurs.

Metal: One of a class of elements that includes a large majority of the known elements; metals are characteristically lustrous, malleable, ductile, and good conductors of heat and electricity.

Metallic bond: The force of attraction that holds metals together; it consists of the attraction of free-flowing valence electrons by positively charged metal ions.

Metamorphic rock: Rock formed from other rocks as a result of intense heat, pressure, or chemical change.

Metamorphism: The changing of one type of rock to another by heat, pressure, and chemical activity.

Meteor: A piece of rock or dust falling through the Earth's atmosphere.

Meteorite: A piece of rock or metal from space that has impacted the Earth.

Meteoroid: A chunk of dust, rock, or metal that is smaller than an asteroid. They may originate from particles blasted off an asteroid by the impact of other meteoroids, or they may form as ice evaporating from a comet that releases dust particles.

Microfilaments: Long thin fibers that give a cell shape, form, motility

Microtubules: Stiff hollow fibers that give cell shape, form, and motility

Mineral: Naturally occurring, inorganic, crystalline solids found in the Earth's crust.

Mitochondria: The cellular organelle within which cellular respiration takes place; where energy is produced for cellular function

Mitosis: Cellular division resulting in two identical copies of the original cell

Mixture: A combination of two or more substances that are not chemically combined

Molecular compound: A compound that is composed of molecules

Molecule: A neutral chemically bonded group of atoms that act as the smallest unit of a substance and retain the properties associated with that substance

Molten: Melted; it is generally used for materials with high melting temperatures, such as rocks or iron.

Moraine: A moraine is sediment deposited as a direct result of glaciation.

Mutation: A spontaneous change in a gene or chromosome

Natural resources: Resources provided by the universe, at the present time primarily by the Earth and sun that are necessary for the survival or comfort of living things. These include air, water, soil, other living organisms, nutrients, rocks, and minerals.

Neap tide: A tide with the least difference between the high and low tides is known as a neap tide.

Nerve cells: Part of the nervous system that enables the body to sense the environment and respond to stimuli

Neutralization: A reaction in which an acid and a base react in an aqueous solution to produce a salt and water

Neutron: A subatomic particle with no charge found in the nucleus of an atom

Newton's first law of motion: A body at rest remains at rest and a body in motion continues to move at a constant velocity unless acted upon by an external force

Newton's second law of motion: A force, **F,** acting on a body gives it an acceleration, **a,** which is in the direction of the force and has magnitude inversely proportional to the mass, *m,* of the body: **F** = *ma.*

Newton's third law of motion: Whenever a body exerts a force on another body, the latter exerts a force of equal magnitude and opposite direction on the former.

Newton's universal law of gravitation: All objects having mass attract each other with a force that is directly proportional to the product of their masses and inversely proportional to the square of the distance that separates them:

$$F = G\,\frac{m_1 m_2}{D^2}$$

Nitrogen Cycle: the pathway where nitrogen moves through an ecosystem

Nonmetal: One of a class of elements that are not lustrous and are generally poor conductors of heat and electricity; nonmetals are grouped on the right side of the periodic table.

Nonrenewable resources: Natural resources that exist in the Earth's crust in a fixed amount and may not be able to be replaced or can be replaced only by geological, physical, or chemical processes that may take hundreds of millions of years.

Nuclear fission: The splitting of the nuclei of large atoms, usually uranium-235, into smaller nuclei along with the release of energy.

Nuclear fusion: The combination of the nuclei of small atoms to form a larger nucleus along with the release of energy.

Nucleon: A nuclear particle; a proton or a neutron

Nucleus: The dense central portion of an atom; composed of protons and neutrons

Nucleus: A large cellular organelle that contains DNA

Nuclide: A specific variety of an element's isotopes

Occluded front: The boundary formed when a fast-moving cold air mass overtakes and lifts a warm air mass, completely cutting it off from the ground.

Octet rule: Atoms react by gaining or losing electrons so as to acquire the stable electron structure of a noble gas, usually eight valence electrons.

Ohm's law: A law that states that the current and resistance in a circuit are inversely proportional. It also states that voltage and current are directly proportional.

Ohms: A unit of resistance or opposition to current flow. Resistance or opposition to current flow depends on four factors: the kind of conductor, the length of the conductor, the cross-sectional area of the conductor and the temperature of the conductor.

Öort cloud: A spherical region surrounding the solar system beyond the orbit of Pluto that contains the nuclei of comets.

Organic sedimentary: Rock formed from the remains of organisms.

Original horizontality: The principle that states that all sediment (with minor exceptions) was deposited horizontally is called original horizontality.

Osmosis: A specific form a diffusion involving the movement water from a region of higher concentration to a region of lower concentration

Outwash plane: An area at the front of a glacier where material is deposited by streams originating as water melting off the glacier.

Oxidation: A process that involves a complete or partial loss of electrons or a gain of oxygen; it results in an increase in the oxidation number of an atom.

Oxygen-Carbon cycle: The repeated movement (cycle) through the environment of Carbon and Oxygen with in an ecosystem

Ozone: A form of atmospheric oxygen that has three atoms per molecule.

Paleozoic era: The Paleozoic era extends from 540 to 245 million years; this is the time in which life began to flourish in the sea and moved onto the land.

Parsec: The distance from Earth that an object would be if it appeared to shift by one second of arc ($\frac{1}{3600}$°) over the course of 6 months (approximately 3.26 LYs).

Passive transport: The transport of a substance across a semi permeable membrane; does not require energy, because the movement is from a region of higher concentration to lower concentration

Penumbra: The outer part of a shadow where the light source is not completely blocked.

Period: A period is a subdivision of a geologic era.

Period: A period is the length of time it takes one object to orbit another.

Perpetual resources: Natural resources that no matter how much they are used will never be depleted, such as solar or wind energy.

Petrochemical: Any chemical derived from petroleum.

pH: A number used to denote the hydrogen-ion concentration, or acidity, of a solution; it is the negative logarithm of the hydrogen-ion concentration of a solution.

Phenotype: The appearance of an individual due to the expression of certain alleles

Photosphere: The visible light surface of the sun is known as the photosphere.

Photosynthesis: The process by which plants, algae, and cyanobacteria make their own food, through the conversion of carbon dioxide and water into glucose

Photovoltaic cell: A device that converts sunlight into electricity (solar cell).

Physical change: An alteration of a substance that does not affect its chemical composition

Physical property: A quality of a substance that can be observed or measured without changing the substance's chemical composition

Phytoplankton: Microscopic ocean plants.

Pitch: In music and acoustics, it refers to the frequency of a given tone.

Polar zone: Areas on Earth where solar radiation strikes at a low angle, resulting in temperatures that are nearly always cold. Polar zones extend from 66.5° north and south of the equator to the poles.

Polyatomic: A tightly bound group of atoms that behaves as a unit and carries a charge

Precambrian era: The Precambrian era extends from the formation of the Earth 4.6 billion years ago, up to the 540 million years ago. The era in which Earth formed, the oceans and continents formed, and life first evolved.

Precipitation: The process by which water falls from clouds to the Earth as rain, snow, sleet, and hail.

Producer: Organisms that photosynthesize and produce their own food

Product: A substance formed in a chemical reaction

Prominence: Arcs of gas within the sun's corona, which form within the magnetic field between sunspots, is known as prominence.

Proton: A positively charged subatomic particle found in the nucleus of an atom

Pure substance: A sample of matter having a uniform and definite composition; it can be either an element or a compound.

Radiation: The penetrating rays emitted by a radioactive source; also, the giving off of energy in various forms such as heat, light, or radio waves.

Radio telescope: An instrument that uses a radio receiver and antenna to observe celestial objects.

Radioactive decay: Emission of atomic particles at a constant rate from a radioactive substance and its resulting change into other elements is known as radioactive decay.

Radiometric dating: A process used to determine the absolute age of a rock or fossil by determining the ratio of parent nuclei to daughter nuclei within a given sample.

Reactant: A starting substance in a chemical reaction

Recessive allele: The allele that is not expressed in the phenotype when present together with the dominant allele in an individual

Recycling: Reusing previously manufactured parts or materials.

Red shift: The apparent shift of an element's absorption lines toward the longer, redder, wavelengths.

Reduction: A process that involves a complete or partial gain of electrons or the loss of oxygen; it results in a decrease in the oxidation number of an atom.

Reflecting telescope: A type of telescope that uses mirrors to gather and focus visible light.

Refracting telescope: A telescope that uses lenses to gather and focus visible light.

Regional metamorphism: Metamorphism that affects rocks over large areas during periods of tectonic activity.

Relief: The difference in elevation between the highest and lowest points in an area.

Renewable resources: Natural resources such as trees, air, or freshwater, which, because they are naturally recycled or self-sustaining, can be used indefinitely.

Reservoir: A supply of water stored for future use. It is usually formed by damming streams.

Revolution: The movement of one object around another object such as the orbit of satellites around Earth or the orbit of the Earth around the sun.

Ribosome: Cellular organelle responsible for protein synthesis

Richter scale: The scale that measures the magnitude of an earthquake.

Rift valley: A steep, narrow, fault-created valley formed as lithospheric plates separate.

Rock cycle: The combination of processes that change rocks from one type to another and back again.

Rotation: The spinning of an object around its axis.

Runoff: The water that flows over the land into streams and rivers is called runoff.

Sandbar: A long ridge of sand deposited by wave action just off shore.

Saturated: Air that contains all the water vapor it can hold at a specific temperature.

Sediment: Solid, fragmented material that originates from weathering of rocks

Sedimentary rock: Sedimentary rock is formed from the hardened deposits of sediment.

Series: A row of elements in the periodic table of the elements

Sheet erosion: A process in which parallel layers of topsoil are stripped away by running water, exposing the underlying subsoil or partially weathered bedrock.

Shoreline: A place where the ocean and land meet (beach).

Solar collector: A device that uses sunlight to heat water.

Solar flare: A powerful eruption of particles and radiation from the surface of the sun.

Solar wind: The constant flow of ionized particles away from the sun.

Sound: A longitudinal wave created by compression and expansion of the gas molecules in air

Spectroscope: A device that uses prisms or diffraction gratings to break light into its individual wavelengths.

Spectrum: The arrangement of visible light ordered according to wavelength.

Speed: A measure of the rate of change of distance with respect to time. It is the distance traveled divided by the time needed to travel that distance.

Spit: A long, narrow deposit of sand connected at one end to the shore, generated by wave action and longshore currents.

Spring tide: A tide with the greatest difference between the high and low tides.

Station model: A cluster of weather symbols plotted on a map indicating the weather conditions at a particular reporting station.

Stationary front: The boundary formed when two air masses meet and neither is displaced.

Strain: A change in the shape or volume of rocks due to stress.

Stream load: The total amount of sediment and dissolved minerals carried by a stream.

Stress: Any force that causes pressure in the rocks of the Earth's crust.

Subduction: The process by which one lithospheric plate slips beneath another lithospheric plate.

Sublimation: The process by which a solid changes directly into a vapor.

Summer solstice: The first day of summer in the Northern Hemisphere. At noon, the sun is located directly over the Tropic of Cancer. This typically occurs on June 21.

Sunspot: A darkened, cooler region on the photosphere of the sun where magnetic fields have slowed the convection of hot plasmas from the sun's interior.

Superposition: The principle that in undisturbed rock layers, the oldest rock layers are at the bottom, and the newest layers are at the top.

Temperate zone: Areas on Earth that extend between 23.5° and 66.5° north and south of the equator. Temperate zones have moderate temperatures.

Terminal moraine: Sediment deposited at the leading edge of a glacier.

Terrestrial planet: Any of the first four planets that resemble Earth in their relatively small size, rocky crusts, and metallic cores are known as terrestrial planets.

Tidal bulge: The distortion of the Earth due to the gravitational influence of the moon or sun or due to the revolution of the Earth's center of mass around the center of mass of the Earth-moon system.

Tidal range: The difference between the height of the water at high and low tides.

Tides: The rising and falling of the surface of a moon or planet due to its interactions with another object. Usually it refers to the rise and fall of an ocean as seen at the shoreline.

Tombolos: Sandbars or gravel bars that may connect an island with another island or an island with the mainland.

Topographical map: A map that shows the surface features of an area.

Topography: The surface features of the Earth or other planet.

Transform plate boundary: A place where two lithospheric plates slide horizontally past each other.

Transpiration: The movement or flow of water vapor by living organisms is known as transpiration.

Tropics: The area 23.5° north (Tropic of Cancer) or south (Tropic of Capricorn) of the equator where the sun is almost directly overhead.

Umbra: The dark inner portion of a shadow where the light source is completely blocked.

Unconformity: A break in the geologic record created when rock layers are removed by erosion before new sediments are deposited is known as unconformity.

Uniformitarianism: A theory that states that geologic processes that occur today have been occurring since the Earth was first formed. This theory is often summarized as "The present is the key to the past."

Valence electron: An electron in the highest occupied energy level of an atom

Valley glacier: A long narrow mass of ice that originates in the snow fields of a mountain range and moves down through the mountain's valleys.

Vernal equinox: The first day of spring in the Northern Hemisphere. At noon, the sun is directly over the equator. This typically occurs on March 21.

Volcanism: Any activity that includes the movement of magma toward or onto the Earth's surface.

Volcano: A vent or fissure by which magma reaches the Earth's surface.

Volt: The unit of measurement for voltage. It represents electrical "pressure" or the force with which electrons are pushed through a circuit.

Volume: The amount of space occupied by matter

Waning: The period from the full moon to the new moon when the moon appears to be getting smaller.

Warm front: The boundary formed where a warm air mass overtakes and rises over a cold air mass.

Water cycle: The continuous movement of water from the air to the Earth and back again.

Water cycle: The continuous movement of water between the Earth's surface and the atmosphere through evaporation, condensation, and precipitation.

Watt: The unit of measurement for electrical power. It is the product of voltage and current (amperes).

Wave-built terrace: An extension of a wave-cut terrace that result from the deposition of eroded material off shore.

Wave-cut terrace: A nearly level platform of rock left after the erosion of a sea cliff.

Wavelength: The distance from one wave crest to the next.

Wavelength: The distance between two adjacent crests of a wave

Waxing: The period from the new moon to the full moon when the moon appears to be getting larger.

Weather: The general condition of the atmosphere at a particular time and place.

Weight: A measure of the force of attraction between Earth and an object

Winter solstice: The first day of winter in the Northern Hemisphere. At noon, the sun is directly over the Tropic of Capricorn. This typically occurs on December 21.

Zygote: The cell created by fertilization that contains two complete sets of chromosomes

Practice
Test 1

Practice Test I

Open-Ended Questions

1. Describe the water cycle on a global scale, as illustrated by the diagram below. The numbers in the figure indicate approximate water flow in billion billion (10^8) grams per year.

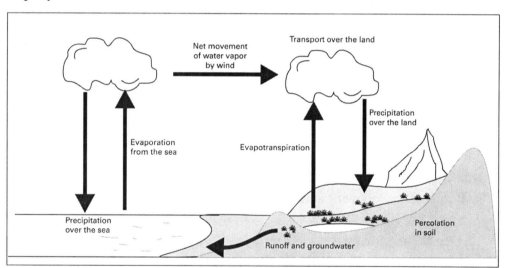

2. After a student mixes an enzyme with its substrate, the amount of product formed is determined at 10-second intervals for 1 minute. Data from this experiment are shown below:

Time (seconds)	0	10	20	30	40	50	60
Product formed (mg)	0.00	0.25	0.50	0.70	0.80	0.85	0.85

Discuss the validity of the student's conclusion that the maximum amount of product produced is after 50 seconds.

3. Mike was walking down the sidewalk toward his home. In a part of his neighborhood they were building a new house, and the builders had surrounded the edge of the property with pieces of black plastic attached to little wooden stakes in the ground. Mike was curious about why the plastic was there, so he asked one of builders working at the site. The builder told him the plastic was there to keep the dirt on the property from washing into the street when it rained.

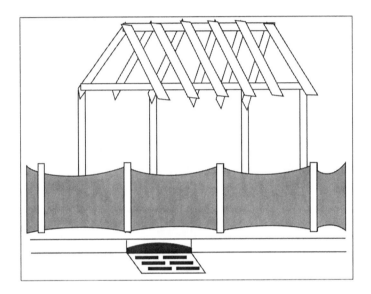

Based on what you know about natural resources, explain why it is important to keep the dirt on the property and out of the street.

Multiple-Choice Questions

1. Which of the following statements regarding the flow of energy and nutrients in an ecosystem is FALSE?
   a. Each time energy is used in an ecosystem, some of it is lost as heat.
   b. Nutrients (nitrogen, phosphorus, carbon) are recycled in a circular flow within an ecosystem.
   c. Energy is recycled in a circular flow within an ecosystem.
   d. Energy moves through an ecosystem in a continuous one-way flow.

2. The green color of most plant leaves is due to the fact that
   a. chlorophyll absorbs green wavelengths of light for use in photosynthesis
   b. chlorophyll reflects green wavelengths of light
   c. carbon dioxide absorbed by leaves absorbs green wavelengths of light for use in photosynthesis
   d. carbon dioxide absorbed by leaves reflects green wavelengths of light

3. Many factors can limit population size. Which of the following population-limiting factors would be considered a density-dependent limiting factor?
   a. The widespread use of DDT prior to the 1970s drastically reduced the size and health of eagle populations.
   b. A local population of foxes declines following an outbreak of a disease that kills 75% of the areas rabbits, the primary food source for the local foxes.
   c. The damming of a river prevents 90% of the salmon from returning to their spawning grounds and reproducing.
   d. Overharvesting decimates the oyster population in the Gulf of Mexico.

4. The increase in DDT concentration at successive trophic levels in a food chain, as illustrated below, is referred to as

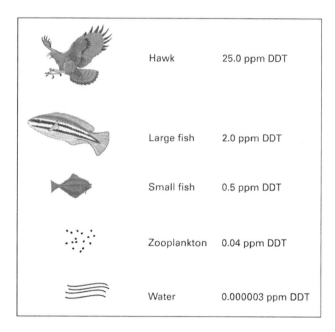

	Hawk	25.0 ppm DDT
	Large fish	2.0 ppm DDT
	Small fish	0.5 ppm DDT
	Zooplankton	0.04 ppm DDT
	Water	0.000003 ppm DDT

   a. biological concentration
   b. biological addition
   c. biological excess
   d. biological magnification

5. Which of the following statements best describes the relationship between genes and proteins?
   a. Genes are the building blocks of proteins.
   b. Genes are composed of proteins.
   c. Genes encode proteins.
   d. Genes are equivalent to proteins.

6. If red flower color shows incomplete dominance over white flower color, what ratio of flower colors would you expect to observe among the offspring from the following cross?

$$RR \times rr$$

a. All pink-flowered plants
b. One-half red-flowered plants and one-half pink-flowered plants
c. One quarter red-flowered plants; one-half pink-flowered plants; and one-quarter white-flowered plants
d. All red-flowered plants

7. Natural selection can best be defined as
a. changes that take place in a population over time
b. the mutation rate in a population
c. descent with modification
d. differential success in reproduction among individuals in a population

8. Which of the following statements does NOT provide evidence for the theory of evolution?
a. Species tend to be more closely related to other species in the same area than to species with a similar way of life and environmental conditions but living in a distant area.
b. The succession of fossil forms is compatible with what is known from molecular and biochemical evidence.
c. All living organisms use the same model of genetic inheritance (DNA —> mRNA —> protein) and share the same genetic code.
d. Marsupial mammals are found in both Australia and the United States.

9. Which of the following sets of features is common to both plant and animal cells?
a. Mitochondria and plasma membrane
b. Nucleus and chloroplast
c. Plasma membrane and cell wall
d. Chloroplast and ribosome

10. Erythrocytes are
a. red blood cells responsible for clotting
b. red blood cells responsible for transporting carbon dioxide and oxygen throughout the body
c. red blood cells involved in the immune system response
d. white blood cells responsible for the immune system response

11. Which of the following statements best describes what would happen if a leaf cell from a rose plant and a human blood cell were both placed in distilled water?
    a. Both cells would swell and burst.
    b. Both cells would swell until their cell walls exerted pressure in the opposite direction, preventing the cell from rupturing.
    c. The leaf cell would swell and burst, while the red blood cell would swell until the cell wall exerted pressure in the opposite direction, preventing the cell from rupturing.
    d. The red blood cell would swell and burst, while the leaf cell would swell until the cell wall exerted pressure in the opposite direction, preventing the cell from rupturing.

12. The process of mitotic cell division is crucial for
    a. the repair of damage to tissues
    b. growth of an organism
    c. maintaining genetic continuity from one generation to the next
    d. all of the above

13. Unlike freshwater lakes, oceans have large quantities of dissolved minerals, such as sodium. In the ocean, people find it much easier to float than when they are in fresh water. Why is this?
    a. The salt water has a greater density than fresh water.
    b. People displace a smaller volume of fresh water than salt water.
    c. Fresh water is denser causing people to sink.
    d. This effect is only imaginary because floating depends on the skill of people.

14. Water wheels are used to convert the energy of moving water into a more useful form. In most cases, there are three steps in this process. The energy is in a different form at each step. Which of the following flowcharts shows the most likely order of the energy changes?
    a. water energy →mechanical energy →solar energy
    b. water energy →thermal energy →mechanical energy
    c. water energy →solar energy →electrical energy
    d. water energy →mechanical energy →electrical energy

15. When an acid and a base react with each other _____ and _____ are produced.
    a. salt and CO_2
    b. hydrogen and heat
    c. salt and water
    d. heat and oxygen

16. Vaccines are effective against infectious agents because they
    a. act as antigens
    b. stimulate an immune response
    c. stimulate immunological memory
    d. all of the above

17. The chemical properties of an element are determined by its
    a. atomic mass
    b. proton number
    c. electron arrangement
    d. atomic size

18. Study the table below. Which atom has a net positive charge?

Atom	No. Protons	No. Neutrons	No. Electrons
A	6	6	6
B	25	26	27
C	55	59	54
D	1	0	1

    a. Atom A
    b. Atom B
    c. Atom C
    d. Atom D

19. Oxygen has an atomic number of 8. Which of the following elements would you expect to be MOST similar to oxygen in terms of its chemical properties?
    a. Nitrogen (N)
    b. Fluorine (F)
    c. Sulfur (S)
    d. Chlorine (Cl)

20. Some lakes, such as the Great Salt Lake, accumulate soluble minerals, especially salt. In those lakes, people find it much easier to float than when they are in fresh water. Why is this?
    a. The salt water has a greater density than fresh water.
    b. Salt particles help suspend the body.
    c. Fresh water is denser causing people to sink.
    e. This effect is only imaginary because floating depends on the skill of people

21. Which substance cannot be decomposed into simpler substances?
    a. Ammonia
    b. Aluminum
    c. Methane
    d. Methanol

22. Under the same conditions of temperature and pressure, a liquid differs from a gas because the particles of the liquid
    a. are in constant straight-line motion
    b. take the shape of the container they occupy
    c. have no regular arrangement
    d. have stronger forces of attraction between them

23. The phase change represented by the equation $I_2 (s) \longrightarrow I_2 (g)$ is called
    a. sublimation
    b. condensation
    c. melting
    d. boiling

24. An egg is placed over the mouth of a bottle while a paper burns inside. After the fire goes out, the egg pops into the bottle. The best explanation for this is
    a. the egg reacts with carbon dioxide
    b. carbon dioxide is produced
    c. oxygen is used up which lowers the air pressure in the bottle
    d. carbon dioxide is produced and oxygen is used up

25. Which of the following is not a problem associated with acid rain?
    a. destruction of marble and limestone antiquities
    b. thinning of the ozone layer
    c. loss of aquatic life
    d. corrosion of steel bridges

26. Which of the following uses a *nonrenewable* energy source?
    a. windmill
    b. hydroelectric dam
    c. gasoline engine
    d. solar-heated house

27. The part of a municipal water treatment plant that kills bacteria is
    a. flocculation
    b. settling tank
    c. screening
    d. prechlorination

28. The part of a municipal water treatment plant that removes large particles and objects is
    a. screening
    b. aeration
    c. sand filtration
    d. flocculation

29. Materials such as iron or nickel that are used to make permanent magnets are called
    a. north poles
    b. electromagnets
    c. ferromagnetic
    d. good electrical insulators

30. An electric motor does which of the following?
    a. Converts electrical energy into mechanical energy
    b. Uses the principle that electric current and a magnetic field interact
    c. Can contain an electromagnet
    d. All of the above

31. Mitochondria are used to produce energy for cells. Which type of cell would contain the most mitochondria?
    a. fat cells
    b. bone cells
    c. red blood cells
    d. muscle cells

32. The rock cycle describes how rocks can turn from one type into another. What process is responsible for turning buried sediments into magma?
    a. volcanism
    b. deep burial
    c. uplift
    d. erosion

33. Mitosis, the process by which the nucleus of a cell divides into two nuclei, each containing a complete set of the cell's chromosomes, is essential to life because it
    a. contains four stages for gametes.
    b. maintains genetic continuity from
       one generation to the next.
    c. controls cell functions to ensure successful development.
    d. provides energy for the cells.

34. Which of the following characteristics of carbon allow it to form so many different compounds?

    a. It is a relatively small atom.

    b. It is an extremely common element.

    c. It has equal numbers of protons and neutrons.

    d. Its outer shell of electrons is half full.

35. Combustion involves the chemical combination of a fuel and

    a. oxygen

    b. heat

    c. carbon

    d. nitrogen

36. Combustion of fossil fuels does not result in release of

    a. inert gases

    b. water

    c. carbon dioxide

    d. carbon monoxide

Questions 37–38

The picture below shows different types of electromagnetic radiation hitting Earth.

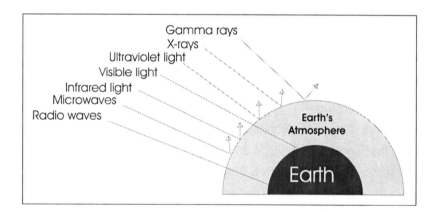

37. Based on this picture, it is reasonable to conclude that Earth's atmosphere filters out all but which of the following types of electromagnetic radiation?

    a. X-rays and microwaves

    b. Radio waves and visible light

    c. Gamma rays and ultraviolet light

    d. Visible light and infrared light

38. If a student were to set up a telescope on the ground, the only type she could use would be
    a. a visible light telescope
    b. an x-ray telescope
    c. a microwave telescope
    d. an ultraviolet telescope

Questions 39–40

Tanisha noticed that the writing on some of the gravestones in the graveyard by her house was almost impossible to read, while on others it was very clear. She started to compare gravestones of the same age, to see if the difference in the clarity of the writing was just the result of age. She also compared the materials out of which the gravestones were made, to see if that was causing the difference. Her results are summarized in the chart below.

Age	Percentage of Brown Gravestones with Readable Writing	Percentage of Gray Gravestones with Readable Writing
25 years old	100	100
50 years old	100	100
75 years old	85	100
100 years old	60	90
125 years old	45	85
150 years old	25	70

39. Based on the graph above, the difference in the clarity of the writing on the brown gravestones versus the gray gravestones was most likely caused by the
    a. age of the stones
    b. skill of the person who carved the stone
    c. durability of the material on which the writing was carved
    d. price of the stone when it purchased

40. The writing on the gravestones was becoming harder to read over time because the
    a. sun was causing it to fade
    b. stones were being weathered by wind, water, and ice
    c. stones were being eroded by wind, water, and ice
    d. stones were being scratched and scuffed by animals

Questions 41–42

Below is a sketch of the layers of rock in two different cliff faces at two different locations. Include in the sketch are pictures of the fossils found in each layer.

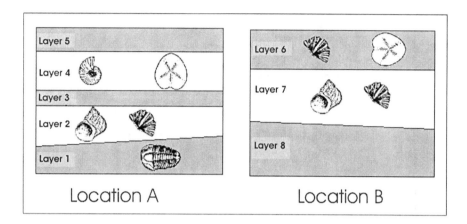

41. Even though these rocks were found at two different locations, which pair of layers probably formed at the same time?
    a. Layers 2 and 7
    b. Layers 5 and 6
    c. Layers 4 and 8
    d. Layers 1 and 6

42. Using the fossil key below, answer the following question.

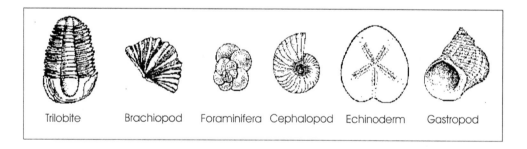

The oldest fossil at Location A is most likely a
    a. gastropod
    b. echinoderm
    c. cephalopod
    d. trilobite

Questions 43–44

Below is a pie graph of the different types of land on Earth.

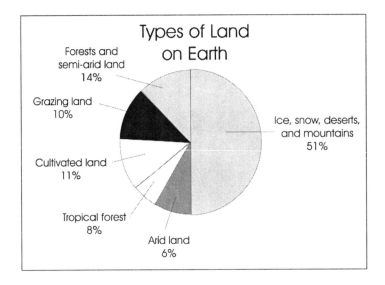

43. Of all the land on Earth, the portion that is being used by humans to produce food is
    a. 50%
    b. 35%
    c. 21%
    d. 10%

44. Based on the graph above, it is important to conserve the good farmland we have because
    a. most of Earth's land is being used for farming already
    b. a large portion of Earth's land is either too hot, too cold, too dry, or too steep to grow crops
    c. we need most of Earth's land to build houses and factories on
    d. more then half of Earth's land is covered by a tropical rainforest

Questions 45–46

Below is a chart showing the amount of nuclear power generated by several countries. The numbers on the graph show how much of the country's total power is supplied by nuclear power.

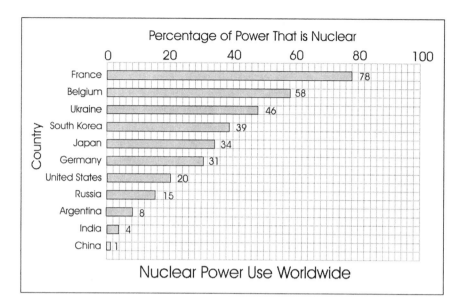

45. Nuclear power use is most prevalent in
    a. Europe
    b. North America
    c. Asia
    d. South America

46. Compared to the rest of the world the United States is among the countries generating
    a. more than half of its power through nuclear power
    b. less than half of its power through nuclear power
    c. less than 10% of its power through nuclear power
    d. none of its power through nuclear power

47. Matt noticed that the air felt warmer when he was standing on his brick patio versus when he was standing in the grass on his lawn. He did some research to find out why there was a difference and found the following information.

Surface Material	Percentage of Solar Energy Absorbed
Soil or rock	90–95
Desert	55–80
Grass	74–84
Forest	80–95
Snow	5–60
Water in the tropics	90–97
Water near the poles	20–90

Based on the information in the chart, Matt can probably conclude that the air over the patio is warmer then the air over the grass because

a. the patio receives more sunlight and reradiates more heat into the air then the grass does

b. the bricks in the patio absorb more sunlight and reradiate more heat into the air then the grass does

c. the grass is green and the patio bricks are red and red things get hotter then green things so the bricks reradiate more heat into the air

d. the grass is living and can maintain a cooler temperature then the patio bricks, which are nonliving, so the grass reradiates less heat into the air

48. The graph below shows the difference in precipitation between the southwest United States and the northeast United States. This difference most likely exists because

a. the southeastern United States receives more intense sunlight then the northeastern United States

b. the southeastern United States is more mountainous then the northeastern United States

c. both of the above

d. neither of the above

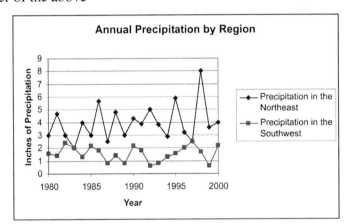

Experimentation Questions

A group carries out the enzyme lab (using pectinase and cellulase to extract apple juice from apple sauce) and collects the following data:

Drops of pectinase	Drops of cellulase	Amount of apple juice collected
0	10	15 mL
10	0	20 mL

1. They conclude that pectinase always works better than cellulase to extract apple juice. The best reason that this conclusion is invalid is:
   a. the group does not carry out enough trials or experiments to make this statement.
   b. they do not keep the number of drops of enzyme constant.
   c. pectinase and cellulase should not be used to extract apple juice.
   d. more juice is collected using cellulase.

2. Another group indicates that they will test various amounts of pectinase and cellulase, but that they will always add a total of 20 drops of liquid to their test tube. This is known as a:
   a. independent variable
   b. dependent variable
   c. controlled variable
   d. experiment

Open-Ended Questions:

Use the information given to answer the questions:
Two groups of students conducted the enzyme experiment and recorded the following:

Group A
Problem:
   • Does the amount and type of enzyme affect the production of apple juice from apple sauce?
Procedure:
   1. Place 5 grams of apple sauce into each of 3 test tubes.
   2. Add 10 drops of pectinase to Tube 1.
   3. Add 10 drops of cellulose to Tube 2.
   4. Add 5 drops of pectinase and 5 drops of cellulose to Tube 3.
   5. Wait 5 minutes, mixing briefly. Then strain each tube of apple sauce through a coffee filter. Measure and record the amount of juice collected.
Data:

Amount of pectinase	Amount of cellulose	Amount of juice collected
10 drops	0 drops	10 mL
0 drops	10 drops	6 mL
5 drops	5 drops	10 mL

Group B
Problem:

The purpose of this lab was to see which enzyme would help us produce the most juice. The independent variable was the enzyme. The dependent variable was the juice.

Procedure:

The procedure was to add each enzyme to apple sauce to see how much juice would be produced.

Data:

Pectinase	Cellulose	Juice
5 drops	5 drops	20 mL
8 drops	3 drops	19 mL
6 drops	4 drops	19 L

3. What conclusions can be drawn from Group A's first experiment and results? How valid do you think these conclusions are, based on the group's experiment and results? Explain your answer fully.

4. Group A concluded that the pectinase always produces more juice than cellulose alone. Is this a valid statement? What additional procedures could they follow to test this conclusion?

5. Group B concluded that the amount of each enzyme does not affect the amount of juice produced. Is this a valid statement? Explain your answer fully.

Practice Test 1 Answers and Explanations

Open-Ended Answers

1. Although most organisms are composed largely of water, very little of the water cycling through an ecosystem is chemically changed by the organisms present, with the exception of the water molecules that are split during the process of photosynthesis. The water used in photosynthesis, however, represents a very small fraction of the water in an ecosystem. The water cycle is more of a physical process than a chemical one—primarily involving changes in state (gas, liquid, solid), than chemical changes. As such, the water cycle is quite different from the nutrient cycles (carbon, nitrogen, phosphorous) operating in an ecosystem. In the water cycle, a global scale, evaporation exceeds precipitation over the oceans, resulting in a net movement of water from the oceans to the land. The water moves as water vapor, carried by prevailing winds, from the ocean to the land. Over land, there is an excess of precipitation relative to evaporation. This net precipitation over land results in the formation of surface and groundwater systems that flow back into the

oceans. Approximately 90% of the evaporation over land is from plant transpiration (loss of water through stomata), with the remaining evaporation coming from surface water and other sources.

2. In order to answer this question to receive the maximum score, the response needs to include a discussion of
   - The lack of a control in the experiments—a benchmark for all the other tests that are performed. For example, the student mixed 10 grams of each and recorded the temperature every 10 seconds. All other reactions are compared to this.
   - The lack of mention of the amounts of substrate and enzyme
   - The lack of mention of any temperature
   - The independent and dependent variables in the experiment

All of these factors could have an affect on the rate of the reaction. A good analysis of data includes all of the above.

3. Student responses must include:
   - The identification of topsoil as a nonrenewable resource
   - A description of what happens as a result of topsoil erosion (i.e., less fertile soil, less vegetation, continued erosion, desertification)

Multiple-Choice Answers

1. **The correct answer is c.** Energy moves through an ecosystem in a continuous one-way flow. Each time energy is used in an ecosystem, some portion of it is lost in the form of heat. Nutrients, such as carbon, nitrogen, and phosphorus, are recycled within an ecosystem by moving in a circular flow through organisms, soils, water, and the atmosphere.

2. **The correct answer is b.** Chlorophyll is a pigment found in the chloroplasts of plant leaves. Pigments are molecules that absorb and reflect different wavelengths of visible light. Chlorophyll absorbs wavelengths of visible light in the blue and red ranges and uses the light energy absorbed to carry out the reactions of photosynthesis. Chlorophyll reflects green wavelengths of visible light, which is why chlorophyll itself appears green. Because chlorophyll is the dominant pigment in most plants' leaves, the leaves will also appear green. The carbon dioxide absorbed from the atmosphere by plant leaves does not absorb or reflect wavelengths of light. It is used in the formation of glucose during the photosynthetic reactions.

3. **The correct answer is b.** Density-dependent factors affecting population size are those factors that limit population size based on the number of individuals in the population. If the primary food source of a population is removed or drastically reduced (as in the case of disease killing 75% of the rabbits, the primary food

source of the foxes in the question), the population will then be too large to be supported by the remaining food source and may begin to decline due to starvation. In other words, the larger the population when the food source is removed, the greater the death rate of individuals due to starvation. The other answers (a, c, and d) are all examples of density-independent factors limiting population size. In all three examples, the death rate was not determined (dependent on) the number of individuals in the population. Such things as the spraying of DDT, the damming of rivers, and the over-harvesting of a species would have the same affect on the population whether the population was large or small to begin with.

4. **The correct answer is d**. Biological magnification is the term used to describe the phenomenon by which substances (such as DDT) become more and more concentrated in the tissues of organisms at each trophic level of the food chain.

5. **The correct answer is c**. Genes are specific regions of DNA that code for specific proteins or portions of proteins (polypeptides). Amino acids are the building blocks of proteins. A set of three bases on the DNA molecule encodes a specific amino acid, or a signal to begin or end transcription of a specific gene sequence.

6. **The correct answer is a**. With incomplete dominance, heterozygous individuals have a phenotype intermediate between the two homozygous phenotypes. Therefore, in Question 6, a cross between an individual homozygous for red flower color (RR) and an individual homozygous for white flower color would produce all heterozygous offspring (Rr) with pink flowers.

7. **The correct answer is d**. Natural selection is one of the mechanisms that drive evolution. It is based on the success with which individuals survive, reproduce, and thus contribute genes to the gene pool of the next generation. Answers a, and c describe the process of evolution, which refers to genetic changes that take place in a population over time, resulting in what Darwin referred to as "descent with modification." Answer c, the mutation rate in a population, contributes to genetic diversity within a population, which is the basis upon which natural selection can take place.

8. **The correct answer is d**. While it is true that marsupial mammals occur in both Australia (kangaroo) and the United States (opossum), the statement does not provide any evidence that evolution has occurred. The other answer choices each illustrate a line of evidence with answer a illustrating biogeographical evidence; answer b illustrating evidence from the fossil record; and answer c illustrating evidence based on molecular homologies.

9. **The correct answer is a**. Both plant and animal cells have mitochondria and a plasma membrane, as well as a nucleus, ribosomes, Golgi bodies, and endoplasmic

reticulum. There are several structures found in plant cells that are not present in animals cells, including chloroplasts (and other plastids), a rigid cell wall, and a large central vacuole (animal cells typically have several smaller vacuoles).

10. **The correct answer is b**. Erythrocytes are the red blood cells responsible for transporting carbon dioxide and oxygen throughout the body. Platelets are the red blood cells responsible for clotting activity. White blood cells (not red blood cells) play the primary roll in immune system response.

11. **The correct answer is d**. Plant cells are surrounded by a rigid cell wall that is permeable to most materials. The plasma membranes of both plant and animal cells are selectively permeable, allowing some materials to pass through, while keeping other material out of the cell. Water readily passes through the plasma membranes of both plant and animal cells. Which direction the water flows—into the cell or out of the cell —depends on the concentration of water inside and outside the cell at any given time. When cells are placed in distilled water, there will be a higher concentration of water outside the cell than inside the cell, due to the presence of dissolved substances in the cell sap. Therefore, when placed in distilled water, cells tend to take up water from their surroundings. In the case of red blood cells, which lack a cell wall, the cell will continue to take up water and stretch until it ruptures. In the case of leaf cells, which have cell walls, the cell will take up water until the plasma membrane pushes against the rigid cell wall. The pressure exerted by the cell wall will not allow excess water to be absorbed by the cell, preventing the cell from rupturing.

12. **The correct answer is d**. Mitosis is a process by which a cell divides to make two exact copies of itself. Mitotic cell division is, therefore, important in maintaining the genetic integrity of cells when cells divide for tissue repair and growth.

13 **The correct answer is a.** Objects float because of a difference in density. Substances that are more dense will tend to sink, while those that are less dense will float. By adding sodium and other minerals to water, the water becomes more dense (more molecules in the same amount of space). Therefore, it is easier to float in salt water.

14. **The correct answer is d**. The kinetic energy of the moving water is used to turn the wheel (mechanical energy) which then generates electrical energy.

15. **The correct answer is c**. While nuclear power plants do result in radioactive waste, they do not use burning and thus do not produce sulfur dioxide or nitrogen oxides, the sources of acid rain.

16. **The correct answer is d**. Vaccines typically use killed or weakened strains of the infectious agent for which immunity is desired. For example, the flu vaccine uses

a killed version of the flu virus. Because the agent used in the vaccine retains its outer coat or cell surface, it acts as an antigen (a foreign body that stimulates the immune system to begin produces antibodies against it). In addition to stimulating the immune system to produce antibodies, the vaccine stimulates immunological memory—the production of memory cells that allow the body to initiate the immune response when presented with the same foreign body in the future.

17. **The correct answer is c.** Outer electrons are involved in the bonding of atoms. In order for chemical reactions to taken place, these electrons must be rearranged.

18. **The correct answer is c.** Atom c is the only atom with more protons (positively charged) than electrons (negatively charged), which results in a net positive charge.

19. **The correct answer is c.** Although a yellow solid, sulfur is chemically similar to the clear odorless gas known as oxygen. Both are in the same row on the periodic table. Both are very reactive due to similar electron arrangements.

20. **The correct answer is a.** By adding salt to water, the mass per unit volume increase which results in a higher density. This allows things that have a lower density, for example, the human body, to float.

21. **The correct answer is b.** Elements cannot be decomposed into simpler substances because an element s one kind of substance. Compounds are composed of two or more elements.

22. **The correct answer is d.** Liquids and gases take the shape of the container they occupy and both have no regular arrangement. Both liquids and gases have particles that are in constant motion, but liquids have a constant volume because the forces of attraction between the particles keep them together. Gases do not have a constant volume and the forces of attraction between particles are weaker.

23. **The correct answer is a.** Sublimation means to go from the solid to gas phase (without passing through the liquid phase).

24. **The correct answer is c.** The partial vacuum resulting from diminished pressure pulls the egg into the bottle after most of the oxygen in the bottle reacts.

25. **The correct answer is b.** The thinning of the ozone layer is generally accepted to be caused by the release of other compounds such as CFC's (formerly used in propellants in hairsprays and refrigerants) which react with ozone converting it into oxygen gas.

26. **The correct answer is c.** The gasoline in a gasoline engine is a fossil fuel, and is thus nonrenewable.

27. **The correct answer is d.** Prechlorination is the step in which chlorine is added to the water. Chlorine, a reactive ion, kills bacteria. This is also the reason that swimming pools are chlorinated.

28. **The correct answer is a.** Screening is a process in which mesh filters strain large particles from water.

29. **The correct answer is c.** Ferromagnetic is the term used for permanent magnets. None of the other choices match the definition although they are related to magnetism.

30. **The correct answer is d.** An electric motor contains all the above descriptions as part of its definition.

31. **The correct answer is d.** Muscle cells require the most energy as they contract and drive movement in the body. Since mitochondria produce the energy by burning glucose, muscle cells need many mitochondria.

32. **The correct answer is b.** Deep burial increases the heat and pressure on sediments, causing them to melt.

33. **The correct answer is b.** Mitosis results in two nuclei that are genetically identical to the mother nucleus.

34. **The correct answer is d.** Since carbon's outer shell is only half full, it is very likely to share electrons with other elements in order to obtain a full outer shell. Carbon can share four times with four separate atoms, or could form double and triple bonds to achieve a full outer shell.

35. **The correct answer is a.** Combustion can only occur in the presence of oxygen, which is one of the reactants in combustion.

36. **The correct answer is a.** The products of combustion are generally carbon dioxide and water, but when burning occurs where there is not enough oxygen, carbon monoxide can also be produced.

37. **The correct answer is b.** Answer a is incorrect because the picture shows both x-rays and microwaves bouncing off the atmosphere. Answer b is correct because the picture shows both radio waves and visible light passing through Earth's atmosphere and hitting the surface. Answer c is incorrect because the picture shows both gamma rays and ultraviolet light bouncing off Earth's atmosphere. Answer d is incorrect because the picture shows the infrared light bouncing off the atmosphere even if the visible light doesn't.

38. **The correct answer is a.** Answer a is correct because visible light is one of the only two types of electromagnetic radiation that can pass through Earth's

atmosphere. In order for the student to see something through the telescope, the type of light at which the student is looking has to reach the telescope on the ground. Since a radio telescope is not a choice, it has to be a visible light telescope. Answer b is incorrect because x-rays cannot pass through the atmosphere; therefore, an x-ray telescope would not be able to "see" anything. Answer c is incorrect because microwaves cannot pass through the atmosphere; therefore, a microwave telescope cannot "see" anything. Answer d is incorrect because ultraviolet rays cannot pass through the atmosphere; therefore, an ultraviolet telescope would not be able to "see" anything.

39. **The correct answer is c.** Answer a is incorrect because when the stones are less then 50 years old the brown gravestone and the gray gravestones are both equally readable. Answer b is incorrect because there is no information provided on the skill of the carver, so that a conclusion cannot be drawn based on the graph. Answer c is correct because over time the gray gravestones maintain their readability better then the brown gravestones, so the material they are made out of must be more resistant to breakdown and, therefore, more durable. Answer d is incorrect because the price of the stone when it was purchased was also not provided on the chart, so a conclusion based on the information provided in the chart cannot involve price.

40. **The correct answer is b.** Answer a is incorrect because the writing on the gravestones was carved into it, not written on it in ink, so it would not be bleached by the sun. Answer b is correct because the stones were broken down, or weathered, over time by wind, water, or ice, resulting in less readable writing. Answer c is incorrect because erosion is the movement of material from one location to another. Since the stones did not move, the deterioration in the writing cannot be caused by erosion. Answer d is incorrect because scratches and scuffs by animals would not result in such a dramatic change in such a relatively short period of time.

41. **The correct answer is a.** Answer a is correct because both layers 2 and 7 contain the same index fossils, which means they were probably formed at the same time. Answer b is incorrect because layers 5 and 6 do not contain the same fossils. Answer c is incorrect because layer 4 and 8 do not contain the same fossils. Answer d is incorrect because layers 1 and 6 do not contain the same fossils.

42. **The correct answer is d.** Answer a is incorrect because the gastropod is not found in the deepest layer, layer 1, and, therefore, cannot be the oldest. Answer b is incorrect because the echinoderm fossil is not found in the deepest layer, layer 1, and, therefore, cannot be the oldest fossil. Answer c is incorrect because the cephalopod fossil is not found in the deepest layer, layer 1, and, therefore, cannot

be the oldest fossil. Answer d is the correct answer because the trilobite fossil is found in the bottommost layer, and based on the principle of superposition, the bottommost layer is most likely the oldest, which means the fossils in the bottommost layer are most likely the oldest.

43. **The correct answer is c.** Answer a is incorrect because the amount of land used for grazing and cultivation does not add up to 50%. Answer b is incorrect because the amount of land used for grazing and cultivation does not add up to 35%. Answer c is correct because the amount of land used for grazing (10%) and the amount of land used for cultivation (11%) add up to 21%. Answer d is incorrect because the amount of land used for grazing and cultivation does not add up to 10%.

44. **The correct answer is b.** Answer a is incorrect because only 11% of Earth's land is being used to cultivate crops. Answer b is correct because half of Earth's land is covered in ice, snow, deserts, or mountains, which are too hot, too cold, too dry, or too steep to grow crops on. Answer c is incorrect because there is nothing on the graph that indicates the amount of land being used to build houses and factories on. Answer d is incorrect because the percentage of Earth covered by tropical rainforests is only 8.

45. **The correct answer is a.** Answer a is correct because countries in Europe account for the top three users of nuclear power and represent 5 of the 11 countries listed. Answer b is incorrect because the only country in North America listed is the United States, and it produces less then a quarter of its power using nuclear power. Answer c is incorrect because only three countries in Asia are listed, and two of them are the last two on the list. The remaining Asian country, Japan, only produces about one-third of its power using nuclear power. Answer d is incorrect because only one of the countries listed, Argentina, is in South America, and Argentina only produced 8% of its power using nuclear sources of energy.

46. **The correct answer is b.** Answer a is incorrect because the United States only produces 20% of its power through nuclear power, which is less then half not more then half. Answer b is correct because the United States produces 20% of its power through nuclear power, which is less then half. Answer c is incorrect because the United States produces 20% of its power through nuclear power, which is more than 10%. Answer d is incorrect because the United States produces 20% of its power through nuclear power, which is more then zero.

47. **The correct answer is b.** Answer a is incorrect because there is no indication in the information provided that the patio receives more sunlight then the grass. Answer b is correct because soil or rock (the bricks are made from clay which is similar to soil) absorbs 90%–95% of the solar energy hitting it and will

reradiate more heat then the grass which only absorbs 74%–84% of the solar energy hitting it and what is does absorbed it used in photosynthesis to make sugar, not reradiated as heat. Answer c is incorrect because there is no information of the chart that the color of the material makes any difference in the amount of solar energy absorbed. Answer d is incorrect because there is no information of the chart that the living versus nonliving nature of the materials makes a difference.

48. **The correct answer is c.** Answer a is incorrect because the amount of sunlight the southwestern United States receives is not the only factor that influences the amount of precipitation it receives, compared to the northeastern United States. Answer b is incorrect because the presence of mountains is not the only factor that influences the amount of precipitation the southwestern United States receives, compared to the northeastern United States. Answer c is correct because the intensity of the sunlight in the Southwest and the presence of mountains, which block moisture from the Pacific from reaching it, both combine to give the Southwest a drier climate then the northeast. Answer d is incorrect because both the intensity of the sunlight and presence of mountains influence the amount of precipitation the Southwest receives.

Experimentation Answers

1. **The correct answer is a.** The group only carries out one trial each with pectinase and cellulose, and further, they only try one amount of each.

2. **The correct answer is c.** When a part of an experiment is kept constant to prevent it from affecting the results of an experiment, this is known as a controlled variable.

3. Student responses should include:

They can draw the conclusion that the presence of pectinase seems to increase juice production.

- the conclusion is valid because:
- they use a consistent and specific amount of apple sauce (5 grams)
- they us a consistent number of total drops of enzyme (10 drops)
- the allow each tube to sit for the same amount of time (5 minutes)

Or, the conclusion is not valid because

- they do only one trial of each tube
- they do not have a control group such as water
- They do not test enough different number of drops of individual enzyme.

4. This is not a valid statement because they have not tested every possible situation. The group could carry out similar procedures (keeping the same controls) while testing other groups such as 5 drops of pectinase with 5 drops of water and 5 drops of cellulose with 5 drops of water.

5. Some possible reasons why this is not a valid statement are:
   - they do not specify how long they waited for each tube
   - they do not specify how they extracted juice
   - they do not ever test each enzyme by itself.

**Practice
Test 2**

Practice Test 2

Open-Ended Questions

1. Explain the processes of transcription and translation, as depicted in the diagram below, and discuss their role in determining the characteristics of an organism. Be sure to include all of the following terms in your answer: DNA, messenger RNA (mRNA), transfer RNA (tRNA), ribosome, nucleus, cytoplasm, gene, codon, anticodon, amino acid, polypeptide, protein.

2. When operating, ordinary incandescent light bulbs produce a lot of heat in addition to light. Fluorescent lightbulbs produce much less heat when operating. If you wanted to conserve electricity in your entire home, which type of bulb should you use? Explain your answer.

3. A student is hiking in the Appalachian Mountains near the border of Connecticut and New York State and finds the following rock.

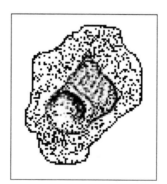

Explain how the fossil of a sea snail could have ended up in the mountains, a seventy-five miles from the nearest large body of water.

Multiple-Choice Questions

1. Nutrients, such as nitrogen or phosphorous, are sometimes limited in an ecosystem due to deforestation, runoff, and other nutrient-depleting processes; however, carbon is usually available in ample quantities because
   a. all organisms can make their own carbon from water and sunlight.
   b. autotrophs can make their own carbon from water and sunlight.
   c. the primary source of carbon is from the soil, where there is a steady supply.
   d. the primary source of carbon is from the atmosphere, where there is typically a steady supply.

2. The equation below represents the process of photosynthesis:

$$6CO_2 + 12H_2O \xrightarrow[\text{chlorophyll}]{\text{light}} C_6H_{12}O_6 + 6O_2 + 6H_2O$$

Which of the following statements about photosynthesis is FALSE?
   a. During photosynthesis, plants take in carbon dioxide from the atmosphere and release oxygen back into the atmosphere.
   b. Plant cells contain chloroplast for carrying out photosynthesis, but lack mitochondria necessary for carrying out cellular respiration.
   c. Plant cells have both chloroplasts for carrying out photosynthesis, and mitochondria for carrying out cellular respiration.
   d. Plants are capable of making their own carbon-based food from carbon dioxide, water, and light energy.

3. The diagram below illustrates the flow of energy within a food web.

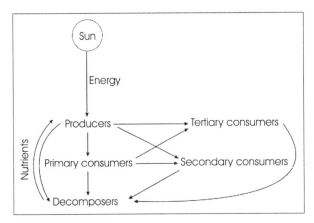

Which of the following organisms would be classified as a producer?
   a. kelp (brown algae)
   b. oak tree
   c. cyanobacteria
   d. all of the above

4. The dramatic increase in levels of carbon dioxide in the atmosphere in recent history is primarily the result of
   a. the combustion of fossil fuels.
   b. a global imbalance between the rates of respiration and photosynthesis.
   c. eutrophication of lakes and streams.
   d. excessive release of chlorofluorocarbons into the atmosphere.

5. Which of the following statements is INCORRECT?
   a. Chromosomes contain DNA.
   b. The building blocks of DNA are nucleic acids.
   c. The building blocks of DNA are amino acids.
   d. Genes are found on DNA and code for proteins.

6. The polymerase chain reaction (PCR) is specifically used to
   a. quickly make numerous clones of a particular segment of DNA.
   b. insert foreign genes into host bacteria cells.
   c. make recombinant plasmids.
   d. produce cDNA libraries.

7. A gene pool can be defined as
   a. a group of individuals belonging to the same species
   b. a group of populations in which individuals have the potential to interbreed and produce offspring
   c. the total complement of genes in a population at a given time
   d. the presence of to or more forms of a character in a population

8. Which of the following represents a modern-day example of evolution by natural selection?
   a. the development of antibiotic resistance in bacteria.
   b. the development of insecticide resistance in mosquitoes
   c. the development of a diversity of beak types among finches on the Galapagos Islands
   d. all of the above

9. Which of the following organelles is INCORRECTLY paired with its function?
   a. chloroplast—photosynthesis
   b. ribosome—protein synthesis
   c. nucleus—ATP production
   d. mitochondria—cellular respiration

10.

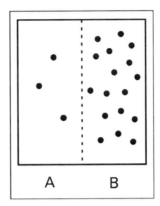

In the above diagram, that depicts two cells separated by a plasma membrane,
   a. solute particles will move across the membrane from side B to side A, until equilibrium is reached
   b. solute particles will move across the membrane from side A to side B, until equilibrium is reached
   c. solute particles will move from side B to side A until all particles are on side A
   d. solute particles will not move across the membrane because side A and side B are already at equilibrium

11. During mitotic cell division, the production of one daughter cell with two copies of each chromosome and one daughter cell with no chromosomes is mostly likely due to a mistake that occurred during
   a. prophase
   b. metaphase
   c. anaphase
   d. telophase

12. A plant that has 12 chromosomes in each of its leaf cells would produce pollen grains containing
   a. 3 chromosomes
   b. 6 chromosomes
   c. 12 chromosomes
   d. 24 chromosomes

13. Which of the following is the best summary of how human activities have contributed to the greenhouse effect?
   a. The heat from burning fossil fuels warms up the atmosphere.
   b. Exhaust gases from burning fossil fuels block sunlight entering the atmosphere.
   c. Sunlight has an easier time penetrating through CO_2 than it does through pure air.
   d. CO_2 and other products of combustion trap radiation attempting to leave the planet.

14. Which of the following is not a result of increased atmospheric CO_2 and global warming?
    a. possible growth of deserts.
    b. changes in distribution of plants and animals
    c. thinning of ozone layer
    d. lengthened growing seasons.

15. Many natural polymers are found in our food, bodies and clothes. Which of the following is not made of a polymer?
    a. a cotton t-shirt
    b. tooth enamel
    c. hair
    d. starch

16. Thermosetting polymers are ones that _____ when heated.
    a. shrink
    b. soften
    c. evaporate
    d. burn

17. The mass of an element is determined mainly by its
    a. atomic number
    b. number of protons and neutrons
    c. electron arrangement
    d. atomic size

18. The atomic number of iron is 26, and the atomic mass is 55.847. What do these numbers mean in regard to protons, electrons, and neutrons?
    a. There are 26 each of protons and neutrons, and the rest of the mass is the result of electrons
    b. There are 26 protons and 26 electrons. Some atoms of iron have 30 neutrons.
    c. There are 26 protons and 29 neutrons. Each particle has an atomic mass of 1.
    d. There are 26 protons and 26 neutrons. Since neutrons have slightly more mass than protons, the mass is greater than 52.

19. When a metal atom combines with a nonmetal atom, the nonmetal atom will
    a. lose electrons and decrease in size
    b. lose electrons and increase in size
    c. gain electrons and decrease in size
    d. gain electrons and increase in size

20. What do the elements carbon, silicon, germanium and tin have in common?
    a. They are metals.
    b. They are in the same period.
    c. They have the same number of electrons.
    d. They have four electrons in their outer shells.

21. During which of the following processes is there a decrease in the heat content of the form of water indicated?
    a. Ice as it forms on a lake
    b. Water droplets as they fall to the ground
    c. Water as it evaporates from a pond
    d. Snow as it melts on a mountainside

22. A log was burned in a fireplace. Which statement is true about the leftover ashes when they are compared to the original unburned log?
    a. The ashes have more mechanical energy than the unburned log.
    b. The ashes occupy the same amount of space as the unburned log.
    c. The ashes have less chemical energy than the unburned log.
    d. The ashes have the same molecular structure as the unburned log.

23. A balanced chemical equation reflects the idea that the mass of the products
    a. is greater than the mass of the reactants
    b. is less than the mass of the reactants
    c. equals the mass of the reactants
    d. is not related to the mass of the reactants

24. In an experiment, 12.0 grams of solid carbon reacted with oxygen gas to form 44.0 grams of carbon dioxide gas. How many grams of oxygen reacted with the carbon?
    a. 12.0 grams
    b. 32.0 grams
    c. 44.0 grams
    d. 56.0 grams

25. One problem associated with landfills is that they
    a. contribute oxygen (a greenhouse gas) to the atmosphere.
    b. contribute methane (a greenhouse gas) to the atmosphere.
    c. contribute acid to the atmosphere.
    d. increase property values.

26. When a bar magnet is cut in half it will
    a. lose all its magnetism
    b. lose the magnetism in one half but not the other
    c. become two smaller magnets
    d. produce separate *north* and *south* magnets.

27. Ionic bonding involves the transfer of electrons from one atom to another. After the transfer, the atoms join together because
    a. they share electrons.
    b. their nuclei share particles.
    c. they no longer are charged.
    d. they are oppositely charged.

28. Nitrogen has an atomic number of 7 and an atomic mass of 14.01. Which of the following is most true of nitrogen?
    a. Each atom of nitrogen has 7 protons and 7 neutrons
    b. Each atom of nitrogen has 7 protons and 14 neutrons
    c. Each atom of nitrogen has 14 protons and 14 neutrons
    d. Each atom of nitrogen has 7 protons and 14 electrons

29. One of the reasons that humans tend to have longer life expectancies in developed countries is that:
    a. people in developed countries eat more processed foods
    b. people in developed countries have more access to methods of birth control
    c. people in developed countries have more access to cell phones
    d. people in developed countries have more access to advanced medical care

30. Two normal parents are both carriers of the recessive gene for cystic fibrosis. If they have a child, we would expect that child to have what chance of having two genes for cystic fibrosis?
    a. 0%
    b. 100%
    c. 75%
    d. 25%

31. A red blood cell is placed into a solution of unknown concentration. After several minutes, the cell shrivels to half its normal size. What is likely true of the beginning concentration of the solution relative to the beginning concentration of the cell?
    a. The solution had a higher concentration of solutes than the cell
    b. The solution had a lower concentration of solutes than the cell
    c. They began at equal concentrations of solutes and water
    d. None of the above

32. The bulbs in a set of holiday lights are arranged in a series circuit. You remove one bulb from the middle of the string. What result would you expect?
    a. The other bulbs will continue to light up when plugged in.
    b. The other bulbs will not light up when plugged in.
    c. The two bulbs on either side of the bulb will not light up, but the others will.
    d. Half of the bulbs will light up.

33. A person can *lose* body weight if the total energy intake
    a. is greater than total energy expended or used
    b. is less than total energy expended or used
    c. is equal to total energy expended or used
    d. is spread out over time, no matter that total energy is expended or used

34. Which condition would result in an increase in the Earth's temperature?
    a. removing water vapor from the atmosphere
    b. increasing the concentration of carbon dioxide
    c. increasing the cloud cover
    d. covering the Earth with snow

35. You are at the beach on a sunny day and observe that the sand gets very hot by midday, while the water temperature remains about the same. Which is the best explanation of this observation?
    a. The cool breeze makes the water feel colder than the sand.
    b. Sitting on the hotter sand makes the water feel cooler.
    c. Sand both absorbs and gives off heat more readily than water.
    d. Hotter sand causes a sea breeze to be produced which cools the water.

Questions 36–38

Brenda was curious about the differences between planets like Jupiter and planets like Earth so she looked up statistics about each. The results of her research are below

Planet	Mass (kg)	Diameter (km)	Density (g/cm3)	Distance from Sun (km)	Average temperature (K)	Rotational period (hr)
Earth	6.0×10^{24}	12,756	5.5	150,000,000	290	23.93
Mars	6.4×10^{23}	6,794	4.0	225,000,000	218	24.48
Jupiter	1.9×10^{27}	142,984	1.3	780,000,000	124	9.84
Saturn	5.7×10^{26}	120,572	0.7	1,440,000,000	97	10.32

36. Based on her research, Brenda can conclude that
    a. the more massive a planet is the denser it is
    b. planets closer to the Sun have shorter rotational periods
    c. planets further from the Sun are colder
    d. planets with large masses have small diameters

37. Brenda found an article in the newspaper describing the discovery of a new planet around a distant star. The planet was called a brown dwarf and was described as being almost 1 billion kilometers from the star and having a high mass. The planet probably also had
   a. a low density
   b. a long rotational period
   c. a high temperature
   d. a small diameter

38. Newton determined that the amount of gravity an object exerts on another object is proportional to the masses of the two objects. Based on this, Brenda could conclude that the planet that exerts the greatest gravitational pull is
   a. Earth
   b. Mars
   c. Jupiter
   d. Saturn

Questions 39–41

Joel drew pictures of three of the rivers in his town. When he drew the pictures, he included not only the river itself, but also a portion of the land around the river, to get a good overall view of each body of water.

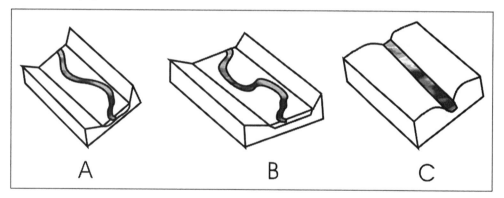

39. Based on his drawing, Joel can probably conclude that
   a. River A is the oldest river in his town
   b. River B is the oldest river in his town
   c. River C is the oldest river in his town

40. River C is most likely located in an area that is
   a. Flat and marshy
   b. Flat and rocky
   c. Steep and rocky
   d. Steep and marshy

41. Based on his drawings and what he knows about rivers, Joel can conclude that
    a. people living along River A are most likely to have problems with flooding
    b. people living along River B are most likely to have problems with flooding
    c. people living along River C are most likely to have problems with flooding
    d. none of people living along these rivers will have significant problems with flooding

Questions 42–44

The chart below shows the irrigation efficiency of three different crop-watering methods used on farms. In a gravity flow system, water piped onto the field and allowed to soak into the low points between rows of crops. In a drip irrigation system a hose is buried under or around the roots of plants and allowed to slowly leak water into the soil. In a center pivot system, a pipe suspended above the crops is swung around while it sprays water onto them.

Type of irrigation	Amount of water that reaches the crops
Gravity flow	60–80%
Drip irrigation	90–95%
Center pivot	80–95%

42. In areas where water is a scarce resource the system that will allow the most water to reach the plants is the
    a. gravity flow
    b. drip irrigation
    c. center pivot

43. On a farm that uses gravity flow irrigation, what portion of every hundred gallons used does not reach the plant?
    a. 20–40 gallons
    b. 5–10 gallons
    c. 5–20 gallons

44. If the average person requires about 1 gallon of water a day to survive, on average how many people could the water wasted by the gravity flow irrigation system supply?
    a. 30 people
    b. 12 people
    c. 7 people

45. Which class of polymers provides the basic building blocks for our bodies?
    a. minerals
    b. fats
    c. proteins
    d. carbohydrates

46. Which is *not* an accurate statement about the foods we consume?
    a. foods supply the human body with energy
    b. the energy supplied by foods is usually measured in units called Calories or kilojoules
    c. Foods, like fossil fuels, contain mostly hydrocarbon compounds
    d. It takes energy to produce food, therefore food can be considered a mechanism for transforming energy

Questions 47–48

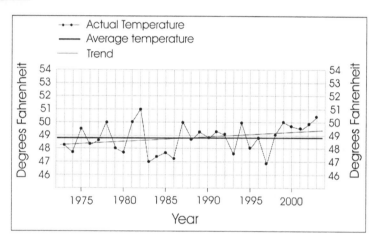

Colorado Springs, Colorado

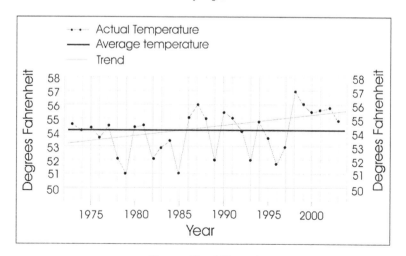

Kansas City, Missouri

47. Colorado Springs, Colorado and Kansas City, Missouri are both located at approximately the same latitude, however, Colorado Springs is in the Rocky Mountains and Kansas City is in the Midwest along the banks of the Missouri River. Kansas City is generally warmer the Colorado Springs because
    a. The sun is out for longer in Kansas City then it is in Colorado Springs
    b. Kansas City is closer to a body of water then Colorado Springs
    c. Kansas City is at a lower elevation the Colorado Springs
    d. Kansas City is closer to a desert then Colorado Springs

48. Over the last 30 years, Colorado Springs has had an average rainfall of 17.4 inches per year while Kansas City has had an average of 37.98 inches per year. Colorado Springs probably gets less rainfall then Kansas City because
    a. It is closer to the equator then Kansas City is
    b. The Rocky Mountains block a lot of the rain from reaching Colorado Springs
    c. The air around Colorado Springs is too thin for it to rain a lot
    d. Colorado Springs is further away from the ocean then Kansas City

Experimentation Questions

Group A carried out the following experiment.

1. Find three pieces of chalk that are all 2 cm long.
2. Get three cups, label them 1, 2, 3 and put 1 cup of vinegar into each one.
3. Heat the vinegar in the first cup up in the microwave until it is 50°C.
4. Cool the vinegar in the third cup down in the microwave until it is 0°C.
5. Put a piece of chalk into each cup and leave it overnight.
6. Take the chalk out of the vinegar and find out what its mass is.

Cup number	Chalk before	Chalk after	Change in chalk
1 0°C	0.62 g	0.83 g	0.21 g
2 25°C	0.65 g	0.82 g	0.17 g
3 50°C	0.61 g	0.77 g	0.16 g

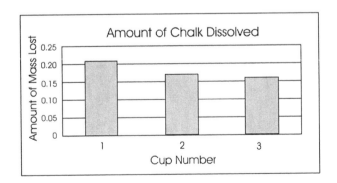

1. Which of the following would best describe the independent variable for **Group A's** experiment?
   a. The mass
   b. The concentration of the acid
   c. The length of the chalk
   d. The temperature of the vinegar

2. **Group A's** experiment would be improved by adding
   a. A second set of trials using different acid concentrations
   b. A second set of trials using the same temperatures
   c. A second set of trials using different sized pieces of chalk
   d. A second set of trials using colored chalk instead of white chalk

Group B got the following results from an experiment they performed.

Size of the chalk	Mass at the beginning	Mass after 24 hours	Change in the mass
1/4 inch	0.33 g	0.12 g	0.21 g
1/2 inch	0.65 g	0.53 g	0.12 g
3/4 inch	1.03 g	0.97 g	0.05 g
1 inch	1.36 g	1.34 g	0.02 g

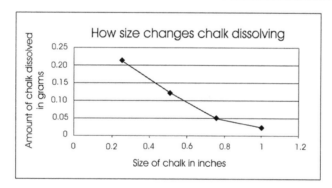

3. Which of the following conclusions is best supported by the data on **Group B's** graph?
   a. As the size of the chalk gets bigger, the chalk weathers more.
   b. As the size of the chalk get bigger, the chalk weathers less.
   c. The size of the chalk doesn't affect the amount of weathering that takes place.
   d. As the size of the chalk gets smaller, the chalk weathers less.

4. A control used by **Group B** was
   a. The size of the chalk used in the experiment
   b. The mass of the chalk used in the experiment
   c. The amount the chalk dissolved by the vinegar
   d. The amount of time the chalk was in the vinegar

The following experiment was carried out by **Group C.**
1. Fill one coffee cup with 100% vinegar
2. Fill a second coffee cup with 50% vinegar
3. Fill a third coffee cup with 100% water
4. Find three pieces of chalk of equal mass
5. Put the chalk in the coffee cup
6. Let the chalk sit overnight
7. Take the chalk out of the coffee cup and let it dry
8. Find out the mass of the chalk
9. Repeat for second trial

Amount of vinegar	Mass of chalk before	Mass of chalk after	Change in mass
0%—Trial 1	1.0 g	0.9 g	0.1 g
0%—Trial 2	1.1 g	1.1 g	0.0 g
50%—Trail 1	0.9 g	0.7 g	0.2 g
50%—Trial 2	1.0 g	0.9 g	0.1 g
100%—Trial 1	1.0 g	0.5 g	0.5 g
100%—Trial 2	1.1 g	0.7 g	0.4 g

5. What valid conclusions can **Group C** draw from their data? Explain fully.
   (*Use separate sheet of paper for open-ended questions.*)

Group D carried out the following experiment. There results are shown below.
1. Measure out nine pieces of chalk that all have a mass of 1 gram
2. Put 3/4 of a cup of 100% vinegar into a coffee cup and heat it up to 30°C in the microwave.
3. Repeat two more times
4. Put 3/4 of a cup of 50% vinegar into a coffee cup and keep it at room temperature (20°C).
5. Repeat two more times
6. Put 3/4 of a cup of 0% vinegar (water) into a coffee cup and cool it to 10°C in the freezer.
7. Repeat two more times
8. Put one piece of chalk into each coffee cup and let them for 24 hours.
9. Take the chalk out of the vinegar and allow it to dry for 24 hours.
10. Find the new mass of the chalk.
11. Repeat step 1–7 for two more trials

Change in Mass - Trial # 1

	100% Vinegar	50% Vinegar	0% Vinegar
30°C	0.7 g	0.5 g	0.1 g
20°C	0.4 g	0.4 g	0.1 g
10°C	0.3 g	0.2 g	0.0 g

Change in Mass - Trial # 2

	100% Vinegar	50% Vinegar	0% Vinegar
30°C	0.8 g	0.4 g	0.0 g
20°C	0.3 g	0.5 g	0.1 g
10°C	0.1 g	0.2 g	0.0g

6. In **Group D's** problem statement, they said they were going to find out the effect of temperature on how fast chalk dissolves." Is this a clear statement of the problem that **Group D** investigated? Explain why or why not.
7. Which group, **Group C** or **Group D**, had a better designed experiment? Explain fully why you think so?
8. Which group, **Group A** or **Group B**, presented their results better? Explain fully why you think so.

Practice Test 2 Answers and Explanations

Open-Ended Answers

1. Transcription is the process by which the genetic code contained in the DNA of an organism is copied (transcribed) into messenger RNA (mRNA). Transcription occurs in the nucleus, and the resulting mRNA moves out of the nucleus into the cytoplasm where it attaches to a ribosome. The ribosome moves along the mRNA three bases (one codon) at a time. Each time a new codon is exposed, a transfer RNA (tRNA) molecule brings in an amino acid based on the message in the codon. Each tRNA molecule binds a specific amino acid on one end and has an anticodon on the opposite end that is complementary to a codon on the mRNA. The tRNA briefly binds to the mRNA. As the ribosome moves along the mRNA, it exposes another site (codon) for a tRNA molecule to bind. The amino acid from the first tRNA is transferred to the second tRNA, where they bind to each other through the formation of a peptide bond. This process continues until the ribosome reaches the end of the mRNA molecule, at which point the ribosome detaches from the mRNA and the newly formed polypeptide. This process of converting the genetic message on the mRNA molecule (copied from DNA) into an amino acid message in a

polypeptide is known as translation. One or more polypeptides make up a protein, and proteins are responsible for the characteristics of an organism.

2. In order to answer this question to receive the maximum score, the response needs to include a discussion of;
   a. the relative amount of light that an incandescent light produces as compared to the fluorescent lightbulb. There is no indication of this in the problem.
   b. the relative number of each type of light used in a home and how this can be factored into energy conservation
   c. the amount of heat each light produces.
   d. a clear description of an experiment the student can perform to determine which type of lightbulb will conserve electricity.
   e. the independent and dependent variables in the experiment.

All of these factors are needed to write a good analysis of the problem.

3. Student responses should contain the following information
   * An explanation of how fossils form that explains the burial process and the change from sediment into sedimentary rock
   * An explanation of how plate tectonics causes rocks that form on the ocean floor to be pushed up onto continents during the subduction of a plate.

Multiple Choice Answers

1. **The correct answer is d.** Carbon enters an ecosystem as carbon dioxide taken up from the atmosphere by autotrophic organisms (producers) and incorporated into their tissues as complex molecules used for energy or storage. The carbon is then passed on to heterotrophs that consume the autotrophs (herbivores), or that consume other heterotrophs (carnivores). Carbon is returned to the atmosphere as carbon dioxide, which is given off by all living organisms during cellular respiration. As long as living organisms are present and respiring, there will be sufficient carbon (in the form of carbon dioxide) available in an ecosystem.

2. **The correct answer is b.** Plant cells contain both chloroplasts, where photosynthesis takes place, and mitochondria, where cellular respiration occurs.

3. **The correct answer is d.** All of the organisms listed are autotrophic—they produce their own food through the process of photosynthesis.

4. **The correct answer is a.** The high rate of combustion of fossil fuels, especially through the use of gas-guzzling automobiles and increased air travel, has significantly increased the carbon dioxide concentration present in the atmosphere. Even if a global imbalance were to occur between the rates of respiration and photosynthesis—which is unlikely to occur on a significant

scale—the excess carbon dioxide in the atmosphere would be minimal compared to that released through the combustion of fossil fuels. Eutrophication of lakes and streams is primarily the result of run off containing high levels of nitrogen and phosphorous, originating from agricultural and urban sources. The release of excessive amounts of chlorofluorocarbons contributes to the destruction of the protective ozone layer surrounding the earth.

5. **The correct answer is c.** Nucleic acids are the building blocks of DNA, whereasamino acids are the building blocks of proteins.

6. **The correct answer is a.** The polymerase chain reaction is one method that can be used to make numerous copies of (amplify) a particular segment of DNA. PCR can be used to make produce a sufficient amount of DNA for extensive testing from a drop of blood or semen, a few skin cells, or a single hair.

7. **The correct answer is c.** A gene pool represents the total aggregate of genes present in a population at a given time. Answer a defines a population; answer b defines a species; and answer d is the definition of a polymorphism.

8. **The correct answer is d.** The overuse of pesticides has allowed for the development of resistant strains of the target organisms, including various strains of bacteria, fungi, and insects. Individuals with genes conferring resistance to a specific antibiotic or pesticide will survive and reproduce, passing along the resistant gene to their offspring. Eventually, resistant individuals will dominate the population and the antibiotic or pesticide in question will no longer be effective. This change in the genetic structure of the population over time can be considered an example of evolution by natural selection. The same can be said for the continuing evolution of various beak types among the finches on the Galapagos Islands in response to the availability of different food sources in different regions.

9. **The correct answer is c.** The nucleus is the organelle that contains the genetic material (DNA) of an organism. ATP is produced during cellular respiration, which occurs in the mitochondria.

10. **The correct answer is a.** In the cell system depicted in the question, solute particles will move across the membrane by diffusion from a region of higher concentration (side B) to a region of lower concentration (side A) until equilibrium is reached (approximately equal quantities of solute on both sides of the membrane).

11. **The correct answer is c.** Anaphase is the phase of mitotic division in which the two sister chromatids are pulled to opposite ends of the cell. If the sister chromatids fail to separate properly, both copies will be pulled to one end of the

cell. Following telophase and cytokinesis, the end result will be one daughter cell containing two copies of each chromosome and one daughter cell with no chromosomes. Neither cell will function normally.

12. **The correct answer is b.** Meiosis is the cell division process that leads to the production of gametes. In order to keep the chromosome number of an organism constant from one generation to the next, meiotic cell division results in the production of gametes with half the number of chromosomes of the organism's somatic cells. Therefore, a plant with 12 chromosomes in each of its somatic cells (e.g., leaf cells) would produce gametes (eggs and sperm) with 6 chromosomes each. In plants, sperms cells are produced by haploid pollen grains, which in this example would have 6 chromosomes.

13. **The correct answer is d.** Carbon dioxide is able to absorb and hold some of the energy from radiation. Under normal conditions on Earth, this ability helps to keep the planet temperate. But when carbon dioxide levels increase, it stands to reason that more carbon dioxide will hold in more of the radiation that would normally reflect back out of the planet's atmosphere.

14. **The correct answer is c.** The thinning of the ozone layer, while also an atmospheric problem, is caused by other factors.

15. **The correct answer is b.** Tooth enamel is made largely of the mineral calcium, not of a polymer.

16. **The correct answer is d.** Thermosetting polymers, such as vulcanized rubber, tend to burn or char when they are heated.

17. **The correct answer is b.** The majority of the mass of an atom is located in the nucleus. The nucleus is comprised of protons and neutrons thus accounting for the mass of the element.

18. **The correct answer is b.** The atomic number (26) of an element indicates the number of electrons and protons. The atomic mass (55.847) is rounded off to the nearest whole number (56) and difference between this and the atomic number is determined (30) which is the number of neutrons.

19. **The correct answer is d.** Metals tend to lose electrons (becoming smaller ions) while nonmetals tend to gain electrons and become larger ions.

20. **The correct answer is d.** These four elements are located in the same row on the periodic table which indicates they have the same number of outer electrons.

21. **The correct answer is a.** Ice is formed by **removing** energy from water. The other three involve the **addition** of energy to the water.

22. **The correct answer is c.** The ash has less chemical energy because the energy in the log was **released** during the burning process.

23. **The correct answer is c.** The word **balanced** indicates that the same mass should be present for products and reactants in a chemical equation.

24. **The correct answer is b.** The difference of 44 grams and 12 grams is 32 grams assuming all of the oxygen reacted and no other products were formed.

25. **The correct answer is b.** The microorganisms decomposing the various components of a landfill produce both methane and carbon dioxide, both greenhouse gases.

26. **The correct answer is c.** If a bar magnet is cut in half, it will produce two bar magnets, both with north and south poles.

27. **The correct answer is d.** Electrons are negatively charged. When an electron leaves an atom, that atom will have more protons than electrons and will be positive. The atom that in turn gets that electron will have an extra electron (more than its number of protons) and will be negative. Opposite charges attract.

28. **The correct answer is a.** The atomic number of any atom is its number of protons, and determines its identity. Since the mass of an atom is determined by its protons and its neutrons only, the number of neutrons can be determined by subtracting the atomic number from its atomic mass.

29. **The correct answer is d.** Medical care and preventive medicine are much more widespread in developed nations, and tend to allow people to live longer lives.

30. **The correct answer is d.** Drawing a Punnett Square shows that only one of four children would have cystic fibrosis, while 2 out of 4 will be carriers like their parents.

31. **The correct answer is a.** Since there were more dissolved solutes in the solution and less water in comparison to the cell, water rushed out of the cell in an attempt to equal out the concentrations in a process known as osmosis. This caused the cell to shrivel as time passed.

32. **The correct answer is b.** In a series circuit, electricity travels through one bulb, then through the next, then the next. If one bulb is removed, the circuit is broken, and the electricity cannot make a circuit, and therefore cannot flow.

33. **The correct answer is b.** If one takes in less energy than one expends, then weight will be lost. This is because the body must use energy stores of carbohydrates and/or fats to make up for the energy difference.

34. **The correct answer is b**. CO_2 and several other molecules are able to absorb some of the UV energy from the sun that would otherwise bounce back out of the atmosphere. Increasing the amount of CO_2 increases the amount of absorbed energy.

35. **The correct answer is c**. Because of hydrogen bonding between water molecules, water has a high specific heat. As a result, water is resistant to changes in temperature, while sand is not.

36. **The correct answer is c.** Answer a is incorrect because the information in the chart shows that larger planets are generally less dense. Answer b is incorrect because the planets that are closer to the sun on the chart have longer rotational periods then the planets further away. Answer c is correct because the average temperature of the planets gets lower as the planets get further from the Sun. Answer d is incorrect because the planets with large masses also have large diameters.

37. **The correct answer is a.** Answer a is correct because planets with high masses generally have lower densities, similar to Jupiter and Saturn on the chart. Answer b is incorrect because the planets with the high masses on the chart tend to have shorter rotational periods. Answer c is incorrect because planets that are about a billion kilometers away from the Sun don't have high temperatures. Answer d is incorrect because planets with high masses don't have small diameters.

38. **The correct answer is c.** Answer a is incorrect because Earth does not have the highest mass of the planets listed and therefore does not have the strongest gravitational pull. Answer b is incorrect because Mars does not have the highest mass of the planets listed and therefore does not have the strongest gravitational pull. Answer c is correct because Jupiter does have the highest mass of the planets listed and therefore will have the strongest gravitational pull. Answer d is incorrect because Saturn does not have the highest mass of the planets listed and therefore does not have the strongest gravitational pull.

39. **The correct answer is b.** Answer a is incorrect because river A doesn't have the biggest meanders or the biggest floodplain, which are signs of an older river. Answer b is correct because river B has the biggest meanders and the biggest flood plain indicating that river B is the oldest river. Answer c is incorrect because river C has no meanders and no floodplain indicating that river C is very young.

40. **The correct answer is c.** Answer a is incorrect because rivers with no meanders and no floodplain are not usually found in flat areas. Answer b is incorrect because rivers with no meanders and no floodplain are not usually found in flat areas. Answer c is correct because rivers with no meanders and no floodplains are

usually found in areas that are steep and rocky. Answer d is incorrect because marshes are found in flat areas and river C is most likely in a steep area.

41. **The correct answer is b.** Answer b is correct because river B is the oldest river, with the largest and probably the flattest floodplain. This means that the difference in elevation along the floodplain is probably very low and the water level only has to rise a few feet to submerge the entire plain. Rivers A and C have steeper sides and smaller floodplains, making them less susceptible to large-scale flooding.

42. **The correct answer is b.** Answer a is incorrect because gravity flow irrigation only allows 60–80% of the water to reach the crops. Answer b is correct because drip irrigation allows 90–95% of the water to reach the crops, which is the highest percentage of those listed. Answer c is incorrect because center pivot irrigation only allows 80–95% of the water to reach the crops, which on average is slightly lower then drip irrigation.

43. **The correct answer is a.** Answer a is correct because 100 minus 60 is 40 and 100 minus eighty is 20, so 20–40 gallons doesn't reach the plants. Answer b is incorrect because 5–10 gallons is the amount of every hundred that doesn't reach the crops in drip irrigation. Answer c is incorrect because 5–20 gallons is the amount of every hundred that doesn't reach the crops in center pivot irrigation.

44. **The correct answer is a.** Answer a is correct because the average of 20 and 40 is 30. Answer b is incorrect because 12 is the number of people the center pivot irrigation could supply with water. Answer c is incorrect because 7 is the number of people the drip irrigation system could supply with water.

45. **The correct answer is c.** Proteins make up the physical structures of our bodies, including muscles, transport molecules, and other cellular structures.

46. **The correct answer is c.** Our foods provide us with all of the building blocks of life, because all of our foods come from living things. Foods contain varying amounts of fats, proteins, carbohydrates, and even DNA, along with smaller molecules like vitamins and minerals.

47. **The correct answer is c.** Answer a is incorrect because Kansas City and Colorado Springs are at approximately the same latitude, so they should receive approximately the same amount of sunlight. Answer b is incorrect because both Kansas City and Colorado Springs are in the middle of the country and while Kansas City is close to the Missouri River, neither city is close to a large body of water, which might affect their climate. Answer c is correct because Kansas City is on the Missouri River flood plain which has a very low elevation, where as Colorado Springs is in the Rocky Mountains. Colorado Spring's higher elevation causes it to have colder temperatures. Answer d is incorrect because Colorado

Springs is actually closer to a desert and if that had an effect then Colorado Springs should be the warmer of the two cities and it isn't.

48. **The correct answer is b.** Answer a is incorrect because both Kansas City and Colorado Springs are at the same latitude, which means they are the same distance from the equator. Answer b is correct because the Rocky Mountains force clouds headed toward Colorado Springs to drop their water on the side of the Rocky Mountains facing the Pacific Ocean. Once the clouds make it over the Rocky Mountains, they have very little moisture left to drop on Colorado Springs. Answer c is incorrect because it can still rain at high elevations where the air is thinner, the air just needs to contain moisture. Answer d is incorrect because Kansas City is about as far away from the Gulf of Mexico as Colorado Springs is from the Pacific Ocean.

Experimentation Answers

1. **The correct answer is d.** Answer a is incorrect because each piece of chalk in the experiment weighed about 0.6 gram when they started, so mass isn't a variable they chose to changed when they designed the experiment. Answer b is incorrect because the vinegar they used wasn't diluted with water, so it was probably all the same concentration (although they didn't explicitly state that, making it a flaw in their experimental design). Answer c is incorrect because they stated in their experimental design that all three pieces of chalk were 2 cm long, which means length wasn't a variable because it didn't change. Answer d is correct because their chart clearly shows that they dissolved the chalk at three different temperatures to see what effect that would have on the chalk.

2. **The correct answer is b.** Answer a is incorrect because trying different concentrations of acid will not tell Group A if the information they got about temperature is accurate. Answer b is correct because doing a second set of trials using the same variable, temperature, will allow them to compare results and see if their first set of data was accurate. Answer c is incorrect because trying different sized pieces of chalk will not tell Group A if the information they got about temperature is accurate. Answer d is incorrect because trying different colors of chalk will not tell Group A if the information they got about temperature is accurate.

3. **The correct answer is b.** Answer a is incorrect because the largest piece of chalk in their experiment weathered the least, not the most. Answer b is correct because their biggest piece of chalk only weathered 0.02 gram, while their smallest piece of chalk weathered 0.21gram. Answer c is incorrect because the graph shows that as the chalk gets bigger it weathers less. Answer d is incorrect because the smallest piece of chalk weathered the most.

4. **The correct answer is d**. Answer a is incorrect because Group B changed the size of the chalk, and a control is something that is kept the same. Answer b is incorrect because the mass of each piece of chalk was different, and a control is something that is kept the same. Answer c is incorrect because both the size and the mass of the chalk (two ways to measure the amount) changed, and a control is something that is kept the same. Answer d is correct because each piece of chalk was kept in the acid for 24 hours and since a control is something that is kept the same, then the amount of time the chalk was in the vinegar must be a control.

5. Student responses should include the following
   - As the concentration of the vinegar got higher, the amount of chalk weathered got higher.
   - Their conclusions are valid because
       They used three pieces of chalk with the same mass
       They allowed the chalk to dry before remassing it
       They did two trials for each concentration and got similar results for each

OR

   - Their conclusions are not valid because
       They didn't specify how much liquid was in each cup
       They didn't specify how much time passed
       They didn't specify if all the pieces of chalk were the same length
       They didn't specify the temperature of the liquid during the experiment
       The masses of the chalk weren't exactly the same and since some of the chalk only changed by 0.1 or 0.2 gram, the difference in the original masses could have affected the results

6. Student response should include
   - This is not a clear statement of the problem they investigated because they experimented with both the temperature and the concentration of the vinegar
   - This experiment has two independent variables instead of just one and it is impossible to tell if there results are from the different temperatures of the acid or the different concentrations.

7. Student response should include
   - Group C's experiment was better designed because they tested only one independent variable, where as Group D tested two at the same time. Group D's experiment had some of the controls Group C was missing (i.e. amount of liquid in the cup and the amount of time the chalk was in the vinegar), however, the presence of two independent variables makes Group D's results totally invalid because there is not way to tell if their results are because the acid concentration changed or the temperature of the vinegar changed.

8. Student responses should include
   - Group B's results were presented better because their graph shows the relationship between their independent variable (size of chalk) and the dependent variable (amount of chalk dissolved).
   - Group A's x-axis is not labeled with their independent variable, just their cup number, so there is no way of knowing that it is the change in temperature that lead to their results.
   - Group A's graph does not indicate the unit they used to measure the amount of mass lost.
   - Group B presented their information in a line graph, which is the correct type of graph to use when looking at the relationship between two numerical values (the size in inches and the amount of chalk dissolved in grams).

Printed in the United States
137607LV00003B/2/P

9 781932 635034